GCSE BITESIZE revision

Check and test

Graphic Products

Design and Technology

Terry Bendall

Published by BBC Educational Publishing,
BBC Worldwide Limited, Room A3040, Woodlands, 80 Wood Lane, London W12 0TT

First published 2003   Reprinted september 2003

Terry Bendall/BBC Worldwide (Educational Publishing), 2003. All rights reserved.

Illustrations © Peter Bull, 2003

Extracts from British Standards are reproduced with the permission of BSI under licence number 2003/SK012. British Standards can be obtained from BSI Customer Services, 389 Chiswick High Road, London W4 4AL, United Kingdom (Tel +44 20 8996 9001).

Colour reproduction by Spectrum Colour, England

Printed and bound by Poligrafico Dehoniano, Italy

Contents

Introduction

About GCSE Bitesize

GCSE Bitesize is a revision service designed to help you achieve success in the GCSE exams. There are books, television programmes and a website, which can be found at **www.bbc.co.uk/education/revision**. It's called *Bitesize* because revision is broken down into bite-sized chunks, making it easier to learn.

How to use this book

This book is divided into the 100 essential topics you need to know, so your revision is quick and simple. It provides a quick test for each bite-sized chunk, so you can check that you know it!

Use this book to check your understanding of GCSE Graphic Products. If you can prove to yourself that you're confident with these key ideas, you'll know that you're on track with your learning.

You can use this book to test yourself:

- during your GCSE course
- at the end of the course during revision.

As you revise, you can use *Check and Test* in several ways:

- as a summary of the essential information on each of the 100 topics to help you revise those areas
- to check your revision progress: test yourself to see how confident you are with each topic
- to keep track and plan your time: you can aim to check and test a set number of topics each time you revise, knowing how many you need to cover in total and how much time you've got.

www.bbc.co.uk/revision

GCSE Bitesize website

The GCSE Bitesize Revision: Design and Technology website provides even more explanation and practice to help you revise. It can be found at: **www.bbc.co.uk/education/revision**

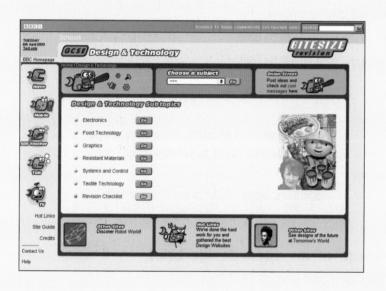

Designing

Check the facts

A design brief is a short statement that tells the designer what will be designed and made.

It should include the following things:

- the nature of the product
- who will use the product
- where the product will be used
- where the product will be sold.

A design brief can be open or closed.

An open design brief allows for a wide range of possible ideas to be developed.

A closed design brief is more specific in what is required.

Example of an open design brief

Design and make a range of greetings cards to appeal to young people aged between 13 and 16 years old, to be sold in a wide range of shops, such as specialist card shops, department stores and stationery shops.

Example of a closed design brief

Design and make a pop-up card that uses a floating layer mechanism and would appeal to 15 to 16 year olds. The card will be sold in a specialist card shop.

Test yourself

Write open and closed design briefs for the following situations:

1 a point-of-sale display for sunglasses

2 packaging for luxury chocolates.

> A specification is a statement that tells the designer exactly what the product has to do and what the design requirements are.

A specification will always:

- describe what the product has to do
- describe what the product will look like
- include details of any other requirements.

In detail, a specification should include the following information about the product:

- the main function of the product
- the main overall dimensions of the product
- the main materials that are likely to be used
- an outline of the appearance of the product
- special considerations or constraints of the users
- if needed, details of the source of power
- how anthropometrics and ergonomics affect the design
- the cost of the product
- possible production levels – one-off, batch, mass production
- legal requirements that may have to be met
- environmental considerations and requirements.

Test yourself

Write a specification for one of the following products:

1 an information guide for the assembly of an item of 'flat-pack' furniture

2 the design of a 'user interface' for a portable CD player.

Designing

BBC GCSE Check and Test: Graphic Products

Check the facts

Designing

> Initial ideas are the possible ideas you have thought of for a product that will meet the requirements of the design brief and specification.

For a GCSE coursework project, you should develop at least ten different ideas, but it is useful if you can think of more than ten.

Where do ideas come from?

It is quite difficult to think of totally new ideas for products. You can develop ideas in the following ways:

- **Evaluating existing similar products** – how well do they do their job? How could they be changed or improved?

- **Doing observational and analytical drawings of products** – looking at patterns from different cultures might provide ideas for lettering styles, while drawings of parts of plants could provide ideas for a board game based on the environment.

- **Thinking about what the product has to do** – what are its attributes? This can be developed from the specification.

- **Brainstorming** – putting down in written or sketch form any possible ideas, however unlikely they might be.

Test yourself

Use the suggestions above to produce three possible ideas for one of the following products:

1 a holder for a 'three pack' of soft drinks cans

2 a disco set for a band playing at a school disco.

Check the facts

Once you have produced a range of possible ideas for a product, you need to decide on one idea to develop.

How to decide which idea to choose

When selecting which idea to develop, you need to look at your design brief and specification and make sure that your idea meets them. There are four important things that you need to think about when developing your chosen idea:

- the shape and form of the product

- the materials that could be used

- the way in which the chosen materials can be cut, shaped and joined

- the finish that could be applied.

You need to research all of the possible methods and decide which one to use. Make sure you give reasons for your decisions in your design folder.

Test yourself

Briefly outline the possible materials and methods of cutting, shaping and joining that could be used if you were developing this design idea for a point-of-sale display for a new children's fiction book.

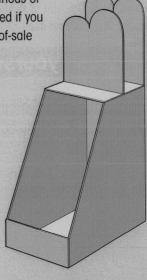

Designing

BBC GCSE Check and Test: Graphic Products

Check the facts

Designing

Materials

Models are often used to develop design ideas in industry and in schools and colleges. Almost any materials can be used for making models. Materials include paper, card, soft wood, such as balsa, obeche or pine, rigid foam, styrene sheet, foam board, construction kits, wire and small sizes of metal rod. Welding rod is good for wire frame models.

Types of models

- Solid block models can be used to show ideas. These are good for product design ideas, such as mobile phones and torches.

- Models in wood, card and foam board are good for flat items, such as point-of-sale displays and interior design.

- Wood and wire are good for models of metal constructions.

- Construction kits are useful to model moving parts. Often, a wide range of materials are combined for models.

Finishes for models

Some models are used to try out ideas quickly and may not need a finish. Models for product design can be painted and made to look very much like the real thing. The type of model and the finish applied will depend on the purpose of the model itself.

Test yourself

Suggest materials for models of the following products:

1 packaging for food products

2 an exhibition stand

3 a user interface for a mobile phone.

Check the facts

> Once an idea has been finalised, you need to plan
> the order of work for making.

You need to think about the following points:

Materials – How long will it take to cut out the
component parts and to shape and join them?

Tools and equipment – How long will you need special
tools, which other people may also want to use?

Processes – How long will it take to do the various
jobs? Include time for glue and finishes to dry.

Components – How long will it take to buy special
components? Will you have to order them in advance?

Health and safety – What are the possible hazards?
How can the risk of harm be reduced?

All of these things need to be fitted into the time that you have to make
the product.

Test yourself

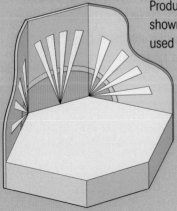

Produce a time plan for making the disco set
shown in the drawing. The main material to be
used is foam board.

Designing

Equipment, model-making and manufacturing

Check the facts

The chart below lists some common items of drawing equipment and their uses.

Item	Description and uses
Drawing board	Used to provide a flat and smooth surface for drawing. Made of wood or plastic.
T-square	Two pieces of wood, or sometimes wood and plastic, screwed together to make a T shape. Used with wooden drawing boards to assist in drawing parallel lines.
Parallel motion	Replaces a T-square on wooden and plastic drawing boards. Used to assist in drawing parallel lines. May be 'built in' to a drawing board.
Set square (two types)	Made from plastic in the form of a triangle. One will give a 45° and a 90° angle. The other will give angles of 90°, 60° and 30°.
Protractor	Made from plastic, either circular or semi-circular. Used to measure angles.
Ruler	Made from wood or plastic. Used for measuring distances and drawing straight lines.
Pair of compasses	Note the correct name. Pencil lead and steel point. For drawing circles and arcs.
Pair of dividers	Note the correct name. Two steel points. For marking distances accurately.
French curves	A range of different-sized curves moulded in one piece of plastic. Used for drawing curved lines accurately.
Flexi curve	Made of flexible plastic with a soft metal core. Can be bent to the desired shape for special lines.

Test yourself

Name the correct item of equipment for the following tasks:

1 measuring an angle of 38°

2 drawing a circle

3 drawing accurate parallel lines.

Check the facts

Colour can be applied to a drawing in various ways. The chart below lists some common methods of applying colour and possible applications.

Item	Description and uses
Graphite pencils	Available in a range of different hardnesses from 9H (very hard) to 9B (very soft). The softer pencils are useful for applying a range of grey and black tones to a drawing.
Coloured pencils	The easiest way to apply colour. Available in a wide range of colours. Good for 'flat' areas of colour, as well as application of texture to a drawing. Water-soluble coloured pencils allow blending of colours.
Felt markers	Can be water based or spirit based. Water-based pens can give good results with practice. Can led to 'streaky' finish if not used carefully. Spirit-based pens are better but need practice. Spirit-based pens need 'bleedproof' paper.
Water colour	Good for application of a 'colour wash'. Practice is needed for good results.
Gouach	A good paint for a thick opaque finish, especially on large areas.
Acrylics	Can be used for opaque areas and to give a colour wash. Good on most materials, including plastics.
Spray paints	Very good for painting 3D models. Use with care. An extraction system may be needed.
Chalks and pencils	Ideal for adding broad areas of colour to a drawing and also tone and shading. Not suitable for fine detail.

Test yourself

Name the most suitable colour media for the following tasks:

1 blending of colour on a 3D drawing

2 applying dense colour to a large area

3 painting a 3D model of a mobile telephone.

Equipment, model-making and manufacturing

BBC GCSE Check and Test: Graphic Products

Check the facts

2D models can be used to show the outline shape of some graphic products. The chart below shows some 2D modelling methods and possible applications.

Item	Description and uses
Sketch drawing	Rough sketches, often drawn on thin paper with a soft pencil or felt markers. Intended to give a rough outline of product ideas.
Flat card models	Useful for 2D products such as greetings cards and pop-ups. May also be useful for signs and user interfaces.
Construction kits	Construction kits are useful for making models of linkages and moving parts in pop-ups and similar products.
Computer modelling	A computer can be used for 2D and 3D work. When used for 2D work, ideas can be drawn on the screen and changed easily. Computers are helpful when it is necessary to try out a large number of ideas.

Test yourself

Name the most suitable type of model for the following applications:

1 trying out ideas for pop-ups in a book

2 trying out the movement in a point-of-sale display

3 showing quickly the rough form of a finished product.

Equipment, model-making and manufacturing

www.bbc.co.uk/revision

Check the facts

3D models can be used to show the outline form of some graphic products. The chart below shows some 3D modelling methods and possible applications.

Item	Description and uses
Fabricated card model	Card is cut and joined to create 3D models. Any type of product that has mainly flat surfaces can be modelled in card – e.g. packaging, room interiors, point-of-sale displays.
Plastic sheet models	May be made from foam board, styrene sheet or corrugated plastic sheet. Product applications as above.
Solid 3D models	May be made from styrofoam or medium density fibreboard (MDF). Used for solid 3D models, such as torches, mobile telephones, radios, etc. These models can be painted and finished to give a very realistic finish. Clay is useful for models that have a lot of curved shapes.
Computer modelling	A computer can be used for 2D and 3D work. When used for 3D work, ideas can be drawn on the screen and different parts can be shown in relation to each other. Useful where moving parts have to be fitted into an enclosure.

Test yourself

Name the most suitable type of model for the following applications:

1 a model of a disco set

2 modelling the movement of a cam and follower inside a box

3 a model of a portable CD player.

Equipment, model-making and manufacturing

BBC GCSE Check and Test: Graphic Products

Check the facts

Screen printing is a way of obtaining multiple copies of a 2D design.

Printing can be done on a wide range of materials, such as fabrics, plastics, paper and card. It is suitable for fairly small numbers – up to a few hundred copies. It is not very good for fine detail. Screen stencils can be made by photographic methods, and these do allow fine details. Normally only one colour is used.

The screen is made of a fine mesh material fixed to a wooden frame. The stencil is laid on the mesh and ink is forced through the cut-out shapes onto the paper below.

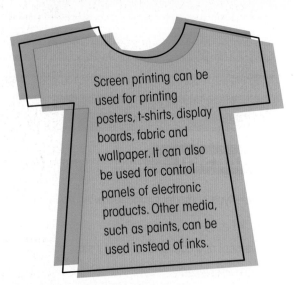

Screen printing can be used for printing posters, t-shirts, display boards, fabric and wallpaper. It can also be used for control panels of electronic products. Other media, such as paints, can be used instead of inks.

Test yourself

1 Name two different products that could be made by screen printing.

2 Why does the screen in a screen-printing process have to be made of a mesh material?

Check the facts

Block printing can be used for small and medium size runs of copies, depending on the material used to make the block.

Printing is usually done on paper and card. Blocks can be made of wood, metal or lino. The shape is cut into the block and ink is applied. The block is then pressed onto the paper. This method is good for repeating patterns. The amount of detail depends on how well the block is made.

Normally only one colour of ink is used. The process if good for making positive and negative images.

Block printing can be used for designs on greetings cards, wall paper, paper table cloths and similar products.

 ## Test yourself

1 Suggest two suitable products that could be made by block printing.

2 Why is block printing not suitable for an image with different colours?

Equipment, model-making and manufacturing

Check the facts

Modern colour printing uses a pattern of dots to make up the image.

- Four colours are used – **black**, **magenta** (red), **cyan** (blue) and **yellow**.

- A **special camera** or **scanner** is used to make printing plates or films that print each of the colours.

- A **screen** is used to change the colours into a pattern of dots that gives the image. Each colour is printed separately.

- **Registration marks** are used to make sure the colours line up.

- Most large runs of colour printing are done on **lithography machines**.

- The order of printing the colours is cyan, magenta, yellow and black.

- A range of colours known as the **Pantone colour range** is used to give special colours. These are defined by their percentage of each of the four colours.

Test yourself

1 Name the four colours used in modern colour printing.

2 Name the printing process used for modern four colour printing.

3 What are registration marks used for?

Check the facts

The table below lists a number of finishing techniques that can be used on graphic products.

Processes	Uses	Costs	Comments
Varnishing Water-based Oil-based Ultra-violet	Protection, Enhancement (e.g. book covers, packaging)	Low cost	Easy process. Ink must be dry. Water-based needs special machine. Oil based is cheapest. Ultra-violet very smooth, but ink must be very dry.
Laminating	Protection, Enhancement (e.g. book covers, packaging, special print jobs)	Expensive	Plastic film applied to the paper or card on one or both sides. Good for protecting products that are handled a lot.
Embossing	Gives visual and tactile effect (e.g. business stationery, invitations, packaging)	Expensive	Requires special press tools to be made. The shape is pressed into the paper or card using steel dies.
Foil applications	Enhancement, Used for special work (e.g. book covers and photograph albums)	Expensive	The design (letters or an image) is stamped on the material through a metal foil. This forces the foil into the surface of the material.

Test yourself

1 Name two methods that could give a protective finish to a graphic product.

2 Which process could be used to give raised lettering on a graphic product?

3 Name examples of products where foil might be used to enhance the appearance.

Equipment, model-making and manufacturing

Check the facts

Photographs are useful in graphics for the following things:

- **Research** – pictures of existing products or locations where products will be used.

- **Recording** how a product is developed.

- **Pictures** of a final product.

You can use:

- A still camera, e.g. a 35 mm camera, and traditional film.

- An 'instant' camera that produces prints straight away.

- A digital camera, where the image can be printed straight away or manipulated using a computer.

The digital camera is the most useful since the image can be seen instantly, the image can be 'imported' into other computer software and films do not have to be processed.

Test yourself

1 Name two types of camera that could be useful in graphic design.

2 Give two reasons why a digital camera is useful for graphics.

www.bbc.co.uk/revision

Check the facts

- **CAD** stands for **C**omputer **A**ided **D**esign
- **CAM** stands for **C**omputer **A**ided **M**anufacturing
- **CNC** stands for **C**omputer **N**umerical **C**ontrol

CAD and CAM are important elements of graphics in industry and in schools and colleges. Some graphic products are designed and made entirely using these two elements.

A CAD/CAM system consists of the following parts:

- **Input** devices, such as a keyboard, mouse, scanner, digital camera, drawing tablet or tracker ball.
- A **processor** – mainly the central processing unit (CPU) of the computer.
- **Output** devices, such as a monitor, printer, plotter, plotter/cutter, CNC lathe, CNC milling machine or stereo lithography machine.

Typical graphics CAD/CAM products:

 2D products

Drawings for making products
Packaging design – developments or nets
Labels for packaging
Standard and pop-up cards
Electronic circuits
Designs for textiles
Information signs
Advertising material
Leaflets, books, pop-up books, information sheets, posters

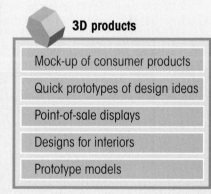 **3D products**

Mock-up of consumer products
Quick prototypes of design ideas
Point-of-sale displays
Designs for interiors
Prototype models

 ## Test yourself

1 Name two input devices and two output devices of a CAD/CAM system.

2 Name two 2D products that could be made using CAD/CAM.

3 Name two 3D products that could be made using CAD/CAM.

Check the facts

Drawing software is of two main types:

Bitmap software

Bitmap software 'draws' in pixels and is equivalent to drawing with a brush on paper. Most clip art is in bitmap format, as are the images from digital cameras. Photo-manipulation software allows images to be altered. Some bitmap software will not allow fine details to be drawn.

Vector software

Vector software 'draws' in coordinates, giving the position, length and angle of lines. This gives much greater control over the image and allows it to be changed more easily. Some vector drawing software cannot easily 'import' bitmap images.

Software can be obtained for 2D drawing and 3D drawing. Some 2D software will allow pictorial views to be drawn on an isometric or oblique grid.

Some advantages of ICT for drawing

- Drawings can be changed and re-sized easily.
- Ready-made drawings can be modified.
- Standard components, such as electrical symbols and architectural symbols, can be imported into a drawing.

Test yourself

1 What is 'bitmap' software?

2 What is 'vector' software?

3 Give two advantages of using ICT for drawing.

Check the facts

Desktop publishing (**DTP**) software allows you to create page layouts that combine text and graphics. These are placed into 'frames' which allow them to be positioned anywhere on the page.

In the past, the text was often created using word-processing software and imported into the DTP software. Today, it is possible to create the text directly in the DTP software if required.

Some modern word-processing software will allow many DTP effects to be created, so the use of separate DTP software may not be needed.

The following effects can be created:

- Text can be styled using a wide range of fonts and effects.

- Different colours of text can be used.

- Background colours can be changed for blocks of text and images.

- Text can be 'wrapped round' images.

- Page layout 'templates' can be set up so that each page has the same appearance.

Test yourself

1 Why is desktop publishing used for graphic design work?

2 Why are frames used in desktop publishing?

Using information and communication technology

BBC GCSE Check and Test: Graphic Products

Check the facts

Information and communication technology (**ICT**) equipment and software can be used to model a product on screen. This allows you to see how the product will look in its surroundings and to change its shape and colour easily. The type of software used depends on what you want to model and how you want to show the object.

ICT modelling in 2D

- Simple 2D drawing software will allow you to change the shape and colour of products.

- DTP software will allow the manipulation of text.

- Text in 2D drawing software can be stretched, reformed and coloured.

ICT modelling in 3D

- Wire frame drawing will show the object by a series of lines.

- Surface modelling shows the surfaces of a product by adding colour and texture.

- Solid modelling shows the finished product as a solid shape.

- Products drawn in 3D software can be re-sized, rotated and tilted.

Test yourself

1 What type of software would be used to model the effect of stretching and rotating text?

2 Why would it be useful to see a solid model of a product such as a mobile phone?

Using information and communication technology

Check the facts

ICT is used for making for the following reasons:

- it allows complex shapes to be made easily and accurately

- changes can be made quickly and easily

- the product can easily be mass produced.

CAM machines used for making graphic products:

2D products

Simple plotter cutters are mainly used for cutting card and vinyl. However, the cutting blade can be replaced with a pen to produce simple drawings and lettering before cutting. Cutter/printers are more complex and allow full colour printing before cutting is done.

3D products

Bench top CNC milling machines are mainly used for cutting plastics, hard wax, wood-based materials such as MDF and soft metals. They are useful for making prototype models, such as craft knives and mobile phones, and for making moulds for vacuum forming. Some of these machines can have a scanner head fitted in place of the cutting tool. This allows 3D scanning to be done.

Test yourself

1 Give two reasons why ICT is used for making products.

2 Why would CAM be useful for making a prototype model of a mobile phone?

Using information and communication technology

BBC GCSE Check and Test: Graphic Products

Check the facts

ICT is used in industry because:

- it can reduce the time taken from ideas to finished product
- changes can be made quickly and easily
- the computer can simulate what the product will look like.

Some industrial uses of ICT, apart from those described in topics 16, 17 and 18, are outlined below.

Stereo lithography

Rapid prototypes can be made by this process. The prototype is divided into very thin layers. A laser beam causes a thin layer of resin in a container to harden. The first layer is lowered into the resin and the next layer set. This process is repeated until the prototype is finished.

Virtual prototyping

The image of the product is drawn with the aid of a computer and software that will give an image as realistic as a photograph. This can be rotated and viewed from any angle.

Making

CNC machines work by the use of electronic data. This information can be sent anywhere in the world by email. Products can be designed in one country and made somewhere else.

Test yourself

1 Give two reasons why ICT is used in industry.

2 Why is virtual prototyping useful?

Check the facts

Terms used:

- **One-off** – only one of a product is made.
- **Batch** – a small quantity of the product is made (two up to about 100).
- **Mass production** – a large number of the product is made, usually on a production line.
- **Continuous flow** – many thousands of the product are made. The difference between this and mass production is that the production line is kept running 24 hours a day, seven days a week.

One-off production is labour intensive. Every product is different.

Batch production may also use a lot of labour, but jigs and templates are used to aid production. Often the machines can easily be changed to produce a batch of a different product.

Mass production often involves the assembly of a number of sub-assemblies of individual components.

Continuous flow is used where the process is automated and few workers are required. It is also used where it would be expensive to start and stop the production process.

Test yourself

Give two examples of products that could be made using each of the production methods described above.

Industrial applications

Check the facts

Vacuum forming

- A mould is made to a suitable shape. Sides of the mould must be tapered from top to bottom.
- The mould is placed in the vacuum-forming machine. A thermo-plastic sheet is clamped in place over the mould and heated.
- When sufficiently hot, the mould is raised up to the plastic. The air below is removed to create a vacuum. Air pressure forces the plastic sheet over the mould.
- When cool, the plastic is trimmed to shape.

Uses – bubble packaging.

Blow moulding

- A metal mould is made in two halves.
- A hollow length of softened plastic is lowered into the mould. The two halves are brought together.
- Air is blown into the plastic to force it into the shape of the mould.
- The product is removed from the mould.

Uses – hollow moulded products, especially 'plastic' bottles.

Test yourself

1 Name types of packaging that could be made by blow moulding.

2 What type of plastic is used for vacuum-forming packaging products?

Check the facts

Injection moulding

- A metal mould is made in two or more parts.
- The mould is clamped into an injection-moulding machine. Softened thermo-plastic granules are forced into the space.
- The product is removed from the mould.

> **Uses** – products with fine detail, e.g. casings for electronic products, bottle caps, 'counters' or figures for board games.

Die casting

- A metal die is made in two or more parts.
- The two halves are clamped together.
- A low-melting point metal alloy is poured into the die.
- When the metal is cool, the two parts of the mould are separated and the product removed.

> **Uses** – metal products with fine detail. Traditional metal type is produced by die casting and blocks for block printing could be produced in the same way. Figures for board games could be made by die casting.

Test yourself

1 Name types of graphic products that could make use of injection-moulded components.

2 What type of plastic is used for injection-moulded products?

Industrial applications

BBC GCSE Check and Test: Graphic Products

Check the facts

Industrial applications

Letterpress is a printing method originally used with moveable type.

It is a type of relief printing where the parts to be printed, both type and illustrations, are raised up from the base plate. Illustrations for letterpress printing are made by a photographic process.

Types of letterpress printing machines are:

Platen press – the paper is pressed against the printing plate with a flat piece of metal called a **platen**. The plate is inked by rollers as the platen is opened.

Sheet-fed rotary press – this has a curved printing surface and can print single sheets at a high speed. Flat sheets are fed between the plate and a pressure roller.

Flat cylinder press – the printing plate is flat and paper is passed over it by a rotary pressure roller.

Uses – uses include small printing jobs such as business cards and business stationery.

Letterpress printing is not used very much now because:

• it uses loose type, which is time-consuming to set up

• the range and style of fonts is limited

• producing the plates for illustrations is time-consuming.

Test yourself

1 Give examples of products that could be printed by the letterpress method.

2 Why is letterpress not used much today?

Check the facts

> **Lithography** **is the most widely used method of printing today and is good for colour work as well as black and white printing.**

The printing plates for lithography are made by a photographic process. The process works on the principle that oil and greasy substances do not mix with water.

> The plate to be printed is coated with a type of grease and then rinsed.

> The plate is then dampened with water and coated with ink.

> The ink only sticks to the parts of the plate that have not been made wet with water.

> The plate is fixed to a cylinder and paper is fed through to give an image.

> **Uses** – medium and long runs for products such as magazines, posters, packaging and book printing.

Offset litho machines work in the same way, but the paper does not come into direct contact with the printing plate, the image being transferred to a rubber roller first.

Test yourself

1 Give examples of products that could be printed using lithography.

2 Why is grease applied to printing plates used for lithography?

Industrial applications

BBC GCSE Check and Test: Graphic Products

Check the facts

Industrial applications

Flexography is similar to letterpress printing and uses a raised-up or relief image.

Flexography uses thin, flexible printing plates made of rubber or photopolymer.

The image on the plates is produced by a photographic process. The inks used are in the form of a thin liquid and dry quickly.

The main use of flexography is for **packaging** since it will print on materials such as cellophane, polythene and metallic films.

Uses – it is used to print 'plastic' shopping bags and packaging used for food products. It is also used to print newspapers and paperback books.

Test yourself

1 Give examples of products that could be printed using flexography.

2 Why is flexography used for printing on food packaging?

Check the facts

Gravure is a printing process that uses printing plates where the image is sunk below the surface of the plate.

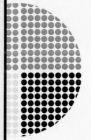

The image is in the form of **small cells** or holes which contain the ink. The cells are filled with ink and the excess is scraped off the surface.

Paper is pressed onto the surface of the plate using a rubber-covered roller that presses the paper into the cells, and therefore in contact with the ink.

Printing plates are usually made from copper and may be produced by engraving or by etching.

Uses – gravure printing is used for high quality, long runs such as magazines, mail-order catalogues, packaging, printing onto fabric and for wall paper. It is also used for printing postage stamps and for decorative plastic laminates, such as kitchen worktops.

Test yourself

1 Give examples of products that could be printed using gravure printing.

2 Why is a rubber-covered roller used in gravure printing?

Industrial applications

BBC GCSE Check and Test: Graphic Products

33

Check the facts

Some printed materials will need to be cut after printing and, if necessary, creased so that they can be folded up. This particularly applies to packaging, but is also used for pop-up cards and books and for 'press-out' shapes which may then be joined together.

Cutting

Cutting is done with a **die cutter**. This is a bit like a paper punch. A punch is made up of cutting blades that will cut out the shape required. A die is used to support the material being cut. This will have a hole or recess for the punch to fit into. The punch and die are fitted into a punching machine, or sometimes a converted letterpress machine is used. The work to be cut is fitted into the machine and the punch lowered down to cut.

Creasing

For creasing, the same idea is used but with blunt blades that will crease the work. Cutting can also be done with a computer-controlled cutter.

Test yourself

Find an example of a package that includes cutting and creasing, e.g. a cereal package. Make a pictorial sketch showing where the two processes would be used.

Industrial applications

Check the facts

A **photocopier** is a very useful tool for **graphic design**. Colour photocopiers are now common and give good results, but the copies are more expensive.

Most copiers will have the following features:

• take a range of different sizes of paper – A5 up to A3

• take card and clear acetate, as well as paper

• will enlarge and reduce

• will do back-to-back copying

• collating of multiple copies can be done.

A photocopier will assist with the following graphic tasks:

• a number of small drawings can be put on a page and copied to give a final sheet

• multiple copies of a drawing can be made and then coloured in different ways

• multiple copies of a drawing can be arranged to explore shape or pattern

• drawings can be enlarged or reduced to fit a space

• reference material can be copied

• artwork sheets to maintain a common style in a project folder can be copied.

Test yourself

1 List three features commonly available on a photocopier.

2 Describe how one of these can be used to assist in the production of a graphic product.

Industrial applications

BBC GCSE Check and Test: Graphic Products

Check the facts

Packaging is used for the following purposes:

- to **contain** and hold the product
- to **protect** the product from damage
- to **inform** the customer about the product
- to create a **product identity** that will help to promote and sell a product
- to make it **convenient** to carry, use and store the product.

The following methods of packaging may be used:

- **glass, plastic bottles** and **jars** are used for liquids, granules and powders
- **boxes** and **cylinders** of card are used for granules, powders and whole items
- **plastic bags** are used for food products and small loose items, e.g. snack foods, sweets
- **metal** (tins) is used for food products
- **vacuum-formed bubble packs** fixed to a card backing are used for small products, e.g. stationery items, toys, screws
- **shrink wrapping** onto a card backing is used for some small products, e.g. DIY products, toys.

Sometimes these are combined.

Test yourself

1 Give three reasons why packaging is used.

2 Give one example of the uses of the following materials/techniques in packaging:
a shrink wrapping
b metal cans
c glass bottles.

Industrial applications

www.bbc.co.uk/revision

Check the facts

> Marketing **is about understanding who the product is for and the sort of products people want.**

> Advertising **is about planning how to tell people about a new or improved product.**

In graphic design, the task may be to design the advertisement for a product or design the packaging for a product, rather than designing the product itself.

Marketing

Market research is used to find out what people want from a product. Market research can use questionnaires, surveys, interviews, test selling and investigation into what other similar products are available for people to buy.

Advertising

Advertising is done through advertisements in newspapers and magazines, on hoardings, radio and television and though the use of leaflets and mail shots. Usually several methods will be used for the same product. The aim is to bring the product to the attention of as many people as possible.

Test yourself

Find an example of a package, e.g. a cereal package, a package for cosmetics or for a toy. List three ways in which the package could be used to advertise the product.

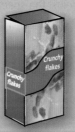

Crunchy flakes

Crunchy flakes

Industrial applications

Industrial applications

Check the facts

In industry, quality is about:

- meeting the specification
- ensuring that the product does what it is supposed to do
- making sure that there are no defects in the product
- making sure that all the products are right first time, every time
- making sure that customers are satisfied with the product.

Quality control is about checking the product at all stages of making to ensure that it meets these criteria.

Testing for quality

Quality needs to be tested at all stages of making a product. Before testing for quality, you need to decide what quality checks are needed and when the work will be checked.

You can test for quality in the following ways:

- Check measurements – are they within the tolerances specified?
- Check the fit of different parts – are they fitted accurately and neatly without gaps?
- Check for appearance – are parts cut and fitted accurately?
- Check for working – do parts move as required? Does the product work as intended?
- Check against the specification – does the product meet all aspects of the specification?

Test yourself

List the quality controls that could be applied to the point-of-sale display unit shown in the drawing.

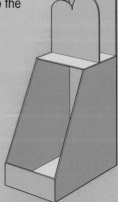

Check the facts

Charts are useful to plan the use of your time, or to plan the making of a product.

There are several different types of planning charts that can be used:

- **Flow charts** describe in words the sequence of operations.
- **Sequence diagrams** show the process of making in words and pictures.
- **Gantt charts** show the tasks involved in making a product and if there can be overlaps in different tasks.

When making a flow chart, remember that Start and Finish boxes are round-ended boxes, processes are put in rectangular boxes and decisions are in diamond-shaped boxes. Flow charts are useful for fairly simple tasks.

Sequence diagrams are useful to show how a task is done, using pictures and notes. They are useful if you need to tell someone else how to do a job or how to use something.

Gantt charts are useful for complex planning, where various tasks can be done at the same time or where two or more people are working on the same product.

Test yourself

Make a sequence diagram for making a pop-up card.

Planning and evaluation

B|B|C GCSE Check and Test: Graphic Products

Planning and evaluation

Check the facts

> There are two sorts of evaluation – evaluation of existing products **and evaluation of** finished products **that you have designed and made.**

Exisiting products

Existing products can be evaluated using several different methods:

1 Using the product. The product is used and the following questions answered:

- Is it easy and convenient to use?
- Does the product do its job?
- Does it appeal to the user?

2 Performance testing. The product is tested to check that it meets its specification and the following questions answered:

- Does it do the job for which it was designed?
- Does it fit into the place where it is used?
- Does it meet other specification requirements?

3 Testing if the product is appropriate. A check is made to see if the product works and meets the needs of the users and the environment. The following checks are made:

- Does it suit the needs of the users?
- Are the materials used transported over long distances?
- Is it made in the local area?
- Are the energy sources and the materials used renewable?
- Is the use of the product and its disposal after use friendly to the environment?

Test yourself

Use one of the methods above to evaluate one of the following products:

1 a pop-up card or book

2 packaging for a box of chocolates

3 an information leaflet or guide.

Check the facts

Finished products

A finished product can be evaluated to check it does the following things:

- meets the design need or situation

- meets the needs of the intended users

- is fit for the purpose for which it is intended.

When evaluating a product to check it meets the needs listed above, you can do some of the following things:

- **Design need**. Look back at your notes to see what the need or situation was. Check to make sure that your product meets this need. For example, if you made packaging for a cosmetic product, does it stand up straight on a shelf? Have all the legal requirements for packaging been met?

- **User needs**. Check that the person who is going to use the product likes the final product. Does it fit into their home? Is the cost appropriate?

- **Fitness for purpose**. Does the product do what was intended? For example, if you made a pop-up book, do the mechanisms work properly?

Test yourself

Look at a product that you have designed and made in the past. Did it meet the needs as described above? List any points not met.

Planning and evaluation

BBC GCSE Check and Test: Graphic Products

Check the facts

Values in design and technology cover the following areas:

Technical values

These include aspects such as accuracy, reliability, methods of making, use of bought-in components, degree of finish required, etc.

Moral values

These include aspects such as the use of sustainable resources, cost of products, images used in a product – do they cause offence? Is the product desirable or needed?

Cultural values

These are concerned with aspects such as lifestyle, fashion, influences of the design of products from other times and cultures, etc.

Environmental values

These are concerned with the source and use of materials, the use of energy and the disposal of waste materials. They are also concerned with pollution and environmental harm caused during making.

How to evaluate a product for value considerations:

Values will vary according to the nature of the product. First, decide what values will be involved in the product you are designing and making. This should be done at the specification stage. Once you know what the values are, you can check to see how well your product conforms to the value issues you have identified.

 Test yourself

List the value issues involved in the design of the following products:

1 a pop-up or other type of greeting card

2 plastic bottles used for soft drinks

3 a board game.

Check the facts

Appropriate use of materials can involve the following aspects:

- Using the most appropriate materials for the **components** of the product. For example, checking that the properties of the material are suitable for the intended purpose. A container for fruit juice needs a foil or wax coating on the inside of a card box to make it waterproof.

- Making sure that material is used **economically**. For example, when making nets for packaging, they can be tessellated to make sure they make the best use of the material.

- Making sure that **processes** are appropriate for the type of material and the use to which the product will be put. For example, printing inks should not come off on your hands.

Often it will be necessary to check by **research** and **testing** that materials have been used appropriately. Include details of how this research was done in your design folder.

Test yourself

Look carefully at your last piece of practical work and the design folder for it. Check the use of materials. List any aspects of designing and making where more appropriate use could have been made of materials.

Planning and evaluation

Check the facts

Appropriate use of processes can involve the following:

- Using **machines** appropriately and with care. Machines can often do a job more quickly and accurately than by hand. The amount of material cut off in one go should not strain the machine or damage it.

- Use **jigs** and **templates** so that making quicker and more accurate where a process has to be done several times.

- Where the same process has to be done on several components, get all the pieces ready for that process. This saves setting up machines a second time.

Often it will be necessary to check by **research** and **testing** that processes have been used appropriately. Include details of how this research was done in your design folder.

Test yourself

Look carefully at your last piece of practical work and the design folder for it. Check the use of processes. List any aspects of designing and making where a more appropriate process could have been used.

Planning and evaluation

Check the facts

The chart below lists a range of graphic materials and possible uses.

Material/description	Uses	Cost
Layout paper Lightweight, white, thin paper.	Used for initial ideas, takes colour media quite well.	Low
Tracing paper Thin, translucent paper.	Making copies of drawings to transfer to other paper/card.	High
Cartridge paper Good quality, white paper available in different weights.	General purpose work, simple models.	Medium
Bleedproof paper	A special paper for work with felt markers.	Medium
Card Range of thicknesses and colours. Thickness range from 300 microns to 650 microns. Metallic finishes available.	Model-making of all types. Thickness used depends on application.	Medium to high
Mounting board High quality, thick card with coloured surface.	Final models. Mounting of finished artwork.	High
Coloured paper A range of different types of coloured paper is available in different thicknesses.	Mounting of work. Also good for applying a coloured surface to models.	Low to medium
Grid paper Available with printed square and isometric grids in different sizes.	Use the grid as a guide for quick sketches and for model-making.	Low

Paper thickness is measured in grams per square metre (**gsm**). This is the weight of one square metre of the paper. Card thickness is measured in microns. One micron is one thousandth of one millimetre.

Test yourself

1 What type and thickness of card would you use for a pop-up model?

2 Why type of paper would be used with felt markers?

Check the facts

The chart below lists a range of materials for model-making and possible applications.

Material	Uses
Card	Pop-ups and other moving models, packaging.
Balsa wood	Fine detail on models, small components.
Foam board	Interior design models, large packaging.
Polystyrene sheet	Vacuum forming, packaging.
Styrene sheet and strip	Product design models where fine detail is needed.
Rigid foam	Product design and solid concept models.
Construction kits	Models with moving parts.
Wood based materials – MDF, plywood, solid timber	Product design and solid concept models. Interior design.
Hard wax	Product design and other 3D models where detail can be carved into shapes.
Plaster bandage	Used with wire support for 3D models where rounded shapes are required.
Metal rod and wire	Any suitable applications where thin, round sections are needed.

 Test yourself

1 Which materials would you use if you were making a concept model of a torch?

2 Which materials would be best to use for a model of a point-of-sale display?

Materials and components

Check the facts

There are a number of different types of plastics materials used for graphic products. The chart below gives details of these and possible applications.

Material/description	Uses
Acrylic Stiff, strong but snaps easily.	Signs, 2D and 3D forms.
Polyvinyl sheet (PVC) Stiff, strong, tough.	2D and 3D shapes, may be vacuum formed. Clear PVC used for blister packs.
High density PVC foam	Machining of 2D and 3D shapes.
Polystyrene sheet	Good for vacuum forming, especially packaging.
Corrugated polypropylene	Stiff but not very strong, good for large constructions.
Acrylonitrile butadienestyrene (ABS)	Square and round tube available in a wide range of shapes and colours, good for structures.
Polystyrene foam	Available in blocks, good for product modelling.
Cellophane	Wrapping round products to provide a seal – often on food products, such as boxes of chocolates.
Polythene	Used for shrink wrapping of products, often onto a card backing.

Test yourself

1 Which materials would you use if you were making a vacuum-formed bubble pack?

2 Which plastics materials would be best to use for a full-sized point-of-sale display?

Materials and components

BBC GCSE Check and Test: Graphic Products

Check the facts

There are a number of different types of adhesive products used when making graphic products. The chart below gives details of these and possible applications.

Adhesive product	Description/Uses
Polyvinyl acetate (PVA)	General purpose glue, mainly for wood but also useful for paper, card, foam board and foam blocks.
Epoxy resin	A two-part glue that has to be mixed together. Useful for joining different materials.
Spray adhesives	Adhesive in an aerosol can, used on large areas of paper and card.
Solvent cements	May be in the form of a stiff liquid, in tubes or cans, or in a thin water-like consistency. Used for joining plastics, especially polystyrene.
Hot-melt glues	Used in a glue gun. Useful for joining different materials.
Glue sticks	A solid stick of PVA based adhesive in a tube.
Adhesive tape (clear)	Single and double-sided. Double-sided very useful for mounting work.
Masking tape	Paper based 'low tack' tape, useful for temporary fixing.
Low tack film	Adhesive film used to make masks for spraying and airbrush work.

Test yourself

1 What type of adhesive would you use when mounting a piece of artwork onto a backing sheet?

2 Give an example of the use of 'low tack' adhesive film.

Materials and components

www.bbc.co.uk/revision

Check the facts

> **The purpose of a model is to represent the finished product.**

The following techniques can be used for finishing:

Paper and card
Make sure edges are straight and that corners are at 90° when required.
Ensure that moving parts work smoothly. Candle wax may help working
parts to move easily.

Corrugated card and plastic
The edges of these materials are difficult to finish. Sometimes, a plastic
strip will help or careful application of PVC tape.

Acrylic
Scrape the edges with a scraper or the edge of a steel rule. Use fine
silicon carbide paper (wet and dry paper). Polish with metal polish.

Foam blocks
Sand gently. May be filled with plaster or wood filler and smoothed.
Use acrylic or water-based paints.

Solid timber and MDF
Sand carefully. May be filled with plaster-based filler or wood filler and
smoothed. Use paint or varnish to give a fine finish. It is usually necessary
to sand down the paint between coats.

Test yourself

1 How should acrylic be finished to give a smooth edge?

2 Describe the finishing processes for a foam block model.

Materials and components

BBC GCSE Check and Test: Graphic Products

Check the facts

Ink consists of a **pigment** or **colourant** that is mixed with a resin, oil or solvent, depending on its use. The substance used is called the **ink vehicle** and determines how fluid the ink is. The type of ink used and how fluid it is will depend on the printing process.

Lithography

Inks for lithography and letterpress printing are in the form of a **paste**. This is to allow the inking rollers to transfer a thin film of ink to the image. The vehicle is slow-drying since the process is relatively slow.

Flexography and gravure

Inks for flexography and gravure are more liquid to allow the cells of the printing plate to be filled up with ink. The solvents used as the ink vehicle allow fast drying because they evaporate quickly.

Screen printing

Inks used for screen printing are between the two described above. They have to be fluid whilst being printed but then have to dry quickly.

> Inks dry after printing partly because the vehicle **evaporates**, and partly because it is **absorbed** into the material being printed.

Test yourself

1 Name the two main parts of printing ink.

2 Why are different types of printing ink required?

Materials and components

Check the facts

The chart below gives details of how lettering can be applied to graphic products.

Materials and components

Method	Description
Self-adhesive paper labels	Usually in the form of individual letters. Used to label individual parts, e.g. keys on a mobile phone. Difficult to get straight – not suitable for extensive work.
Dry transfer lettering	Comes in sheet form. Individual letters have to be rubbed down to the paper. Wide range of fonts. Can be difficult to get straight. Because of the increase in use of ICT, this lettering is not easy to obtain. Useful on models.
Raised plastic letters	Made of styrene. Very useful on solid product design models. Limited range of fonts. Can be painted.
Stencils	May be designed for use with paint and a brush, or with a tubular drawing pen. Styles are limited. Practice is needed to get a good finish. Because of the increase in the use of ICT, this method is now rarely used.
Computer and printer	A good method if the material being used will go through a printer. Range and style only limited by the fonts on the computer. Paper size limited.
Computer and CNC cutter or plotter	A good method for card and vinyl. Larger pieces of work can be produced by cutting out the letters or by using a pen in place of the cutting blade. Plotter allows for different colours.

Test yourself

1 Name two ways of producing lettering on solid product design models.

2 List two advantages and two disadvantages of using computers to produce lettering for graphic products.

BBC GCSE Check and Test: Graphic Products

Materials and components

Check the facts

The chart below gives details of how fastenings and found items can be used for graphic products.

Method	Description
Drawing pins/ mapping pins Dress maker's pins	Drawing pins – useful for fixing paper and card to wooden backing whilst working. Useful for holding parts whilst painting. Mapping pins may be useful to locate information on a chart for a wall display. Dress maker's pins – useful for fixing your work onto display boards.
Paper fasteners/ paperclips	Paper fasteners – useful for moving parts in pop-up books and models. Use with brass eyelets for more robust work. Paperclips – useful to bend into small hooks for models.
Rubber bands and elastic	Useful in pop-up models and crash lock models.
'Found items' are things made for other uses, but which may be useful in graphic products.	Treasury tags – useful to make fastenings on boxes and packaging. Drinking straws – useful for model-making and for making a textured effect. Fabric – useful for interior design for furniture. Model-making parts – toy vehicles, trees, buildings, furniture, model people, to give detail on a model.

Test yourself

1 Give examples of the use of paper fasteners in graphic products.

2 How could rubber bands be used in graphic products?

Check the facts

The chart below gives the key facts about **wheels**, **pulleys**, **gears** and **motors**.

Name	Description	Main uses in graphic products
Wheels	Circular, smooth outside, may be rubber or plastic.	Used for models of vehicles, etc.
Pulleys	Circular with groove round outside edge. Will transmit rotary motion from one place to another over a long distance if required. Different sizes will give different speeds. Axles will need support at each end.	Could be used in 3D working models and similar products to transmit power.
Gears	A gear wheel is a wheel with teeth round the outside which lock into the teeth on an adjacent gear. The teeth are often called cogs. Will transmit rotary motion from one place to another. Different sizes will give different speeds. Axles will need support at each end. Can transmit power through 90°.	Could be used in 3D working models and similar products to transmit power.
Motors	Provide rotary motion from electrical energy. Usually turn at high speed. Gears or pulleys needed to reduce speed.	Useful in point-of-sale and other displays where rotary motion is needed.

Test yourself

1 Compare the use of pulleys and gears in graphic products.

2 How could the output from an electric motor be slowed down to provide a slower speed?

Materials and components

BBC GCSE Check and Test: Graphic Products

Materials and components

Check the facts

The chart below gives the key facts about fastenings used in graphic products.

Name	Description	Main uses in graphic products
Nails and panel pins	May be round wire nails with large head or oval nails with small head.	Limited uses. May be used for joining large pieces of wood or for decorative features on a model.
Wood screws	Round head or countersunk head are available in a range of different metals. May have slot or Posidrive head. Self-tapping screws used with metal and plastics.	Could be used in 3D working models as a pivot for moving parts or for joining wooden or plastics components.
Nuts, bolts, set screws, washers	A set screw has a thread along the whole length. A bolt is only threaded for part of the length. Heads can be hexagon, round, countersunk or pan. Nuts are hexagon shaped. Washers are used to prevent damage to surfaces. Available in a range of metals.	Could be used in 3D working models as a pivot for moving parts or for joining wooden, metal or plastics components.
Rivets	Round head and countersunk rivets hammered over. Pop rivets formed in special pliers.	Limited use in graphic products. May be used in models.

Test yourself

1 Give two uses of wood screws in graphic products.

2 A linkage is made from flat strips of wood 25 mm wide and 4 mm thick. Why would nuts and bolts be better than wood screws for making moving joints?

Check the facts

Sketching is a way of putting ideas down on paper quickly. It should normally be done freehand, but a piece of grid paper may be useful.

- Sketches may be 2D or 3D.

- For complex shapes, sketch a box or series of boxes to give a guide. This is called **crating** or **wire frame** drawing.

- Colour may be used on quick sketches, but its use should be limited. The range of different colours should also be limited.

- Sketching may be done in any medium that you are happy to use. Pencils and fine-line markers are very useful for this.

- The level of detail should show the main points of an idea. Do not show unnecessary detail. Sketches should be sufficiently clear to allow other people to understand your ideas.

- Sketch models or very quick 3D models are useful to show spaces or moving parts. They are made quickly from suitable materials and will usually supplement sketching on paper.

Test yourself

1 Why is crating used when sketching?

2 Why is sketching done freehand?

Graphic techniques and processes

BBC GCSE Check and Test: Graphic Products

Check the facts

Orthographic projection is a way of showing complex objects. This is done by making a 2D drawing of each side to show the main features. Often this will involve a **front view**, a **side view** and a **plan**. However, the number of views used depends on how complex the object is and the amount of detail shown.

Orthographic drawing may be done using **first angle projection** or **third angle projection**. The drawings below show the differences between these.

In first angle projection, the views are on the **opposite side** to the view point. In third angle projection, the views are on the **same side** as the view point.

When doing orthographic projection, a drawing board and parallel motion or a T-square are used to project one view from another. The symbol for each type of projection is shown below the name.

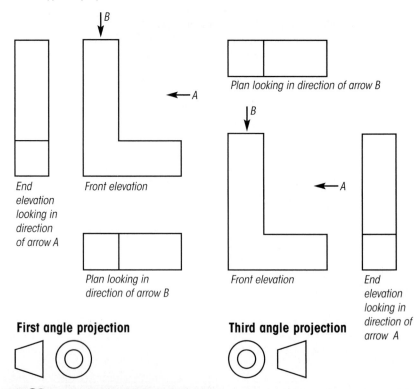

Plan looking in direction of arrow B

End elevation looking in direction of arrow A

Front elevation

Plan looking in direction of arrow B

Front elevation

End elevation looking in direction of arrow A

First angle projection

Third angle projection

Test yourself

1 Why is orthographic drawing used?

2 Draw the symbol for third angle projection.

Check the facts

An assembly drawing shows the various parts of a product drawn as they are fitted together. The parts may be drawn put together or as an **exploded drawing**, which shows the parts separated but in the correct relationship to be fitted together.

Fitted assembly drawings can be drawn in 2D or 3D. Exploded views are usually drawn in 3D. Assembly drawings are often used in products such as construction kits, self-assembly furniture and model kits, to show how things fit together.

Examples of assembly drawings:

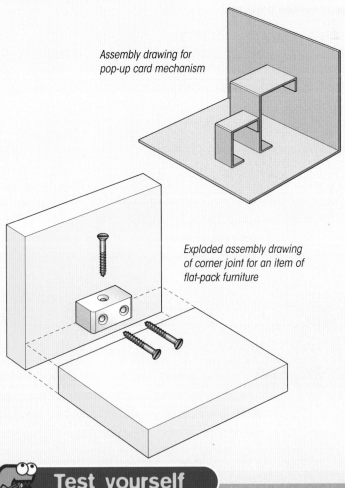

Assembly drawing for
pop-up card mechanism

Exploded assembly drawing
of corner joint for an item of
flat-pack furniture

Test yourself

1 Give three reasons why assembly drawings are used.

2 Describe what is meant by an 'exploded' drawing.

Graphic techniques and processes

BBC GCSE Check and Test: Graphic Products

Check the facts

A section drawing shows the various parts of a product drawn as if they had been cut in two. Sometimes this sort of drawing is called a **cross-section**. The position of the imaginary cut is called a **section plane** and is shown by a special line consisting of long and short dashes.

The purpose of a section drawing is to make the construction of a product clearer. Parts of the object which are cut through are shaded with lines at 45° and spaced 4 mm apart. This is called **cross-hatching**. If two parts of a product are touching, then the cross-hatching goes in opposite directions. Parts, such as nuts and bolts and axles, are not normally sectioned.

Examples of section drawings:

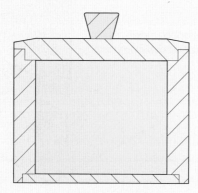

Section view of wooden box showing lid and base

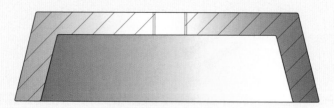

Section view of cast aluminium lamp base with threaded hole

Test yourself

1 Give three reasons why section drawings are used.

2 Describe what is meant by a section drawing.

Check the facts

Isometric drawing is a pictorial drawing method, usually done using drawing equipment.
In isometric drawing, an edge of the object is drawn first and lines are then drawn back at 30°. All vertical lines on an object stay vertical. Lines going back should always be parallel. The drawing on the right shows the principle of isometric drawing.

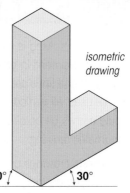

isometric drawing

30°   **30°**

Circles can be drawn in isometric using a grid of lines. The drawing below shows how this is done.

Drawing circles in isometric:

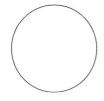

1 Draw the circle.

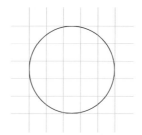

2 Draw a grid of lines over the circle.

3 Draw the grid in isometric.

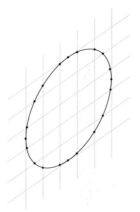

4 Plot where the circle meets the grid, then sketch in the circle.

Test yourself

1 In isometric drawing, what angle is usually used for the lines going back?

2 Describe, using sketches and notes, how a circle is drawn in isometric.

Graphic techniques and processes

BBC GCSE Check and Test: Graphic Products

Graphic techniques and processes

Check the facts

Planometric drawing is a pictorial drawing method, usually done using drawing equipment. In planometric drawing, an edge of the object is drawn first and lines are then drawn back at 45°, although other angles may be used. All vertical lines on an object stay vertical. Lines going back should always be parallel. The drawing below shows the principle of planometric drawing.

Planometric drawings are frequently used to show buildings or room layouts, because they can be drawn directly from a plan view and to scale. In planometric drawings drawn with 45° angles, circles can be drawn with a pair of compasses.

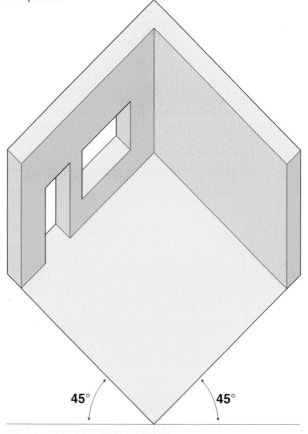

45°   45°

Test yourself

1 In planometric drawing, what angle is usually used for the lines going back?

2 Why is planometric drawing useful for drawings of room layouts?

Check the facts

Perspective drawing is a pictorial drawing method that can be done using drawing equipment and some measuring, or may be done freehand. In perspective drawing, the edge of the object is drawn first. The lines going back gradually come together. If these lines are extended, they will meet at points called **vanishing points**.

Perspective drawing can be one-point, two-point or three-point, depending on the number of vanishing points. **One-point** perspective is often used for room interiors. **Two-point** perspective has many applications for developing ideas in 3D. **Three-point** perspective is often used for drawings of tall buildings.

Perspective drawing is useful because the drawings are more realistic. When we look at objects, they appear to get smaller as the distance from the observer increases.

Single-point perspective of a room interior

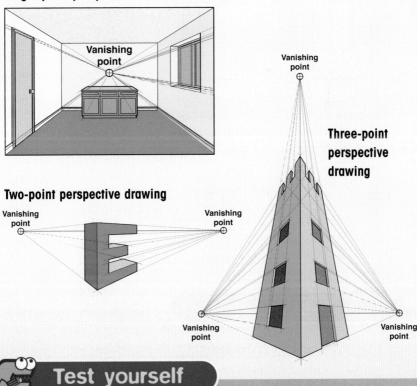

Vanishing point

Vanishing point

Three-point perspective drawing

Two-point perspective drawing

Vanishing point

Vanishing point

Vanishing point

Vanishing point

Test yourself

1 Sketch a cube in two-point perspective. Show the vanishing points.

2 Why is perspective drawing useful?

Graphic techniques and processes

BBC GCSE Check and Test: Graphic Products

Check the facts

Drawing standard components, such as nuts and bolts, gears and pulleys, is time consuming. Because of this, standard symbols have been developed to represent some of these components. These symbols have been produced by the **British Standards Institute** (BSI) and are shown in BS 8888: 2000, a book that shows the symbols to be used. When doing a drawing, the relevant symbols should always be used.

Examples of some common symbols:

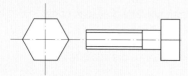

hexagon head screw

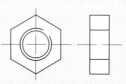

hexagon nut

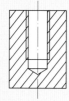

section elevation of screw thread in blind hole

side elevation of screw thread in through hole

compression spring

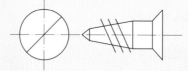

wood screw and self-tapping screw

Test yourself

1 Sketch the symbol for a hexagon nut. Show the side and end elevations.

2 Give the full name of the component shown by the symbol on the right.

www.bbc.co.uk/revision

Check the facts

Dimensions or measurements on a drawing should comply with
BS 8888: 2000.

- Dimensions should be placed outside of the drawing, on a dimension line.
- **Extension lines** are drawn from the object to allow the dimension to be placed away from the drawing.
- If working in pencil, dimension and extension lines should not be as dark as the outline.
- There should be a small gap between the outline and the extension line.
- **Dimension lines** end in arrow heads.
- There should also be a small extension beyond the arrow head and the end of the extension lines.
- Vertical dimensions should be turned so that they can be read from the right.
- Units should be stated.

Other standard conventions are shown in the drawing below.

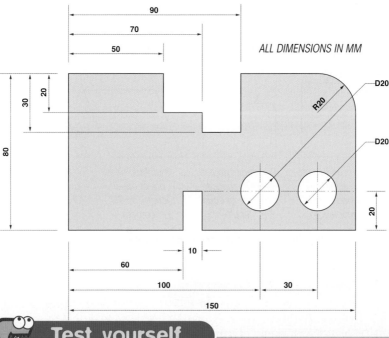

ALL DIMENSIONS IN MM

Test yourself

1 What is the name given to the type of line showing which part of a drawing a dimension applies to?

2 How are vertical dimensions placed on a drawing?

BBC GCSE Check and Test: Graphic Products

Graphic techniques and processes

Check the facts

There are a number of geometrical shapes that you need to be able to recognise. Some of these are shown below.

Triangle

A triangle has three sides. The angles inside a triangle add up to 180°.

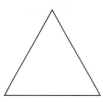 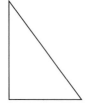 

Equilateral triangle: angles are equal and add up to 180°, sides are of equal length

Right-angled triangle: one angle is 90°

Isocelese triangle: the two sloping sides are of equal length, the two base angels are equal

Accurate triangles can be drawn using a ruler, pencil, set squares and protractor.

Quadrilateral

A quadrilateral has four sides. The angles inside a quadrilateral add up to 360°.

Square: angles are 90°, sides and diagonals are of equal length

Rectangle: angles are 90°, opposite sides are of equal length

Rhombus: sides are of equal length, no 90° corners

Parallelogram: opposite sides are of equal length, no 90° corners

Accurate quadrilaterals can be drawn using a ruler, pencil, set squares and protractor.

Test yourself

1 Describe the properties of a rhombus.

2 Name a triangle that has all sides the same length and all angles the same size.

Check the facts

Some other geometrical shapes are shown below.

Polygon

A polygon is a shape that has more than four sides. A regular polygon has all sides the same length and all angles the same size.

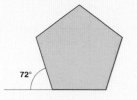 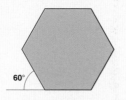 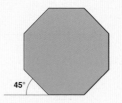

| Pentagon: the exterior angle is 72° | Hexagon: the exterior angle is 60° | Octagon: the exterior angle is 45° |

Accurate polygons can be drawn using a ruler, pencil, set squares and protractor.

Circle and ellipse

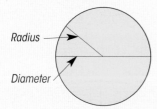 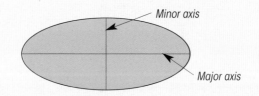

Circle: the diameter is the line that goes all the way across the circle, passing through the centre; the radius is half the diameter

Ellipse: the ellipse has two centre lines called the axies – the major axis is the longer one, the minor axis is the shorter one

A circle is drawn using a pair of compasses. The compasses are set to the radius of the circle. An ellipse is drawn by construction. This is shown in topic 61.

Test yourself

1 Describe the properties of a regular pentagon.

2 Sketch an ellipse, showing the major and minor axies.

Graphic techniques and processes

BBC GCSE Check and Test: Graphic Products

Check the facts

An accurate ellipse can be constructed using a pair of compasses, ruler, pencil and a 30/60 set square. The drawings below show how this is done.

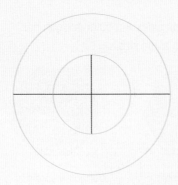

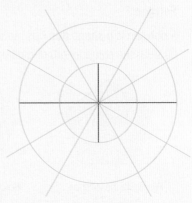

1 Draw the major and minor axies. Draw circles with diameter equal to major and minor axies.

2 Divide the circles up into equal parts using a 30/60 set square.

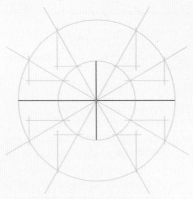

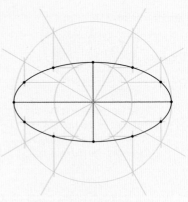

3 Draw vertical lines from where the radial lines cut the large circle. Draw horizontal lines from where the radial lines cut the small circle.

4 Join the points of intersection with a freehand curve.

Test yourself

Practise drawing half an ellipse using the method above.

Check the facts

There are a number of geometrical solids that you need to be able to recognise. Some of these are shown below. Information about each solid is given alongside the drawings.

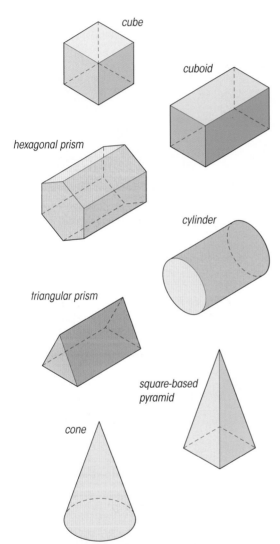

cube

cuboid

hexagonal prism

cylinder

triangular prism

square-based pyramid

cone

CUBE All faces of a cube are squares.

CUBOID The ends are squares. The sides are rectangles.

HEXAGONAL PRISM The ends are hexagons. The sides are rectangles.

CYLINDER The ends are circles. When opened out flat, the side of a cylinder makes a rectangle.

TRIANGULAR PRISM The ends are triangles. The sides are rectangles.

SQUARE-BASED PYRAMID The base is a square. The sides are triangles.

CONE The base of a cone is a circle.

Pyramids can also have bases which are other geometrical shapes, e.g. triangles, hexagons, etc.

Graphic techniques and processes

BBC GCSE Check and Test: Graphic Products

Test yourself

1 Describe the appearance of a triangular prism.

2 Which geometrical shape could be used to make the side of a cylinder?

Check the facts

A development or net is the shape that is cut from sheet material, such as card, to make a 3D form. If the 3D form is made from card, tags have to be added to enable it to be glued together.

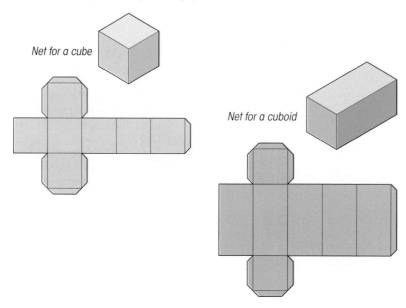

Net for a cube

Net for a cuboid

To draw the net for a cylinder, you need to calculate the length of the side. This is found by using the formula $\pi \times D$.

The ends are made separately and need to have a number of small tags for the glue.

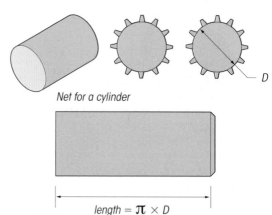

Net for a cylinder

$length = \pi \times D$

Test yourself

1 Describe the appearance of the net for a cylinder.

2 How many sides are needed to make the net for a cube?

Graphic techniques and processes

www.bbc.co.uk/revision

Check the facts

Nets for pyramids and cones are more complicated. The drawings below show how nets for these solids are drawn.

Net for a square-based pyramid

1 Draw the plan and elevation of the pyramid.
Using a pair of compasses, with centre at A, and radius AB, draw an arc to C.

2 Draw line CD vertically to meet the base extended at D.
Draw a line DE. This is the true length of the edge of the pyramid.

3 With centre at E, draw an arc, radius DE to F.
Use compasses to mark off the length of one side of the base round the arc. Mark four steps.
Join from E to these steps.
Finally, draw the base lines.
This gives the net for the pyramid.
Tags for gluing would need to be added.

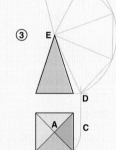

Net for a cone

1 Draw the plan and elevation of the cone.

2 Using a pair of compasses, with centre at A, and radius AB, draw an arc to C.
Use a 30/60 set square to divide the plan into twelve equal parts.

3 Use compasses to mark off the length of one of these divisions round the arc. Mark twelve steps.
Join from A to the last of these steps.
This gives the net for the cone.
Tags for gluing need to be added.

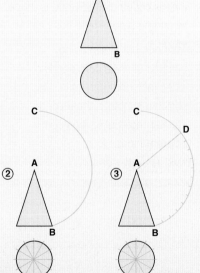

Test yourself

Use the instructions above to draw nets of the pyramid and cone.

Check the facts

There are a range of techniques that can be used to enhance the appearance of a drawing and make it look more like the real object.

Thick and thin lines

For this technique, thick lines are used only where you see one of the adjoining surfaces. The drawings alongside show this idea.

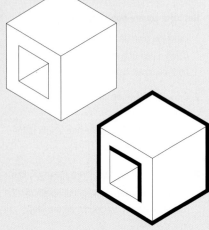

Tone

Tone refers to different shades of the same colour. A lighter tone is called a **tint** and is made by adding white to the base colour. A darker tone is called a **shade** and is made by adding black to the base colour.

Tone can be shown using patterns of lines, dots, shading, reflections and highlights. It is possible to obtain sheets of dry transfer material to represent different tones.

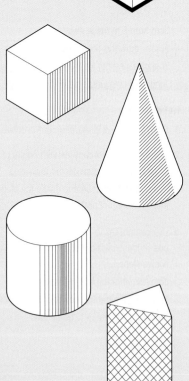

 Test yourself

Use the drawings above to practise the techniques described in the topic.

Enhancement techniques

www.bbc.co.uk/revision

Check the facts

There are a number of ways to show on paper the texture of the materials used to make a product. These are intended to give an impression of the material, rather than represent it exactly. Textures can be in shades of grey or in colour.

Clear plastic and glass
Lines are drawn at an angle to show reflection of light.

Metal
Evenly spaced parallel lines are drawn following the form of the object. Lines are closer in dark areas.

Polished metal
Heavy black lines are used. They reduce in width on lighter areas.

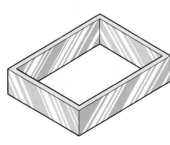

Opaque plastics
Solid colour is used, but some white areas are left to show reflection.

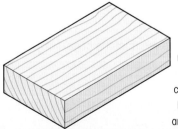

Wood
Thin lines are drawn to represent the grain of the wood. If the drawing is coloured, a light brown can be used as a base colour and a darker shade used for the grain pattern.

Test yourself

Practise using some of the techniques shown in the topic.

Enhancement techniques

BBC GCSE Check and Test: Graphic Products

Enhancement techniques

Check the facts

Colour is an important part of graphic design. You need to know the following facts about colour:

- The **primary colours** are red, yellow and blue.
- The **secondary colours** are made by mixing the primary colours as follows:

  red + yellow = orange
  red + **blue** = **violet**
  blue + yellow = **green**

A colour wheel shows how the colours relate to each other.

- In the colour wheel, colours that are next to each other will **harmonise** (go with) each other.

- Colours on opposite sides of the colour wheel will **contrast** with each other. These are known as **complementary colours**.

- Mixing primary and secondary colours together creates **tertiary colours**. These are dark browns, greens and greys.

- Yellow, orange and red are known as **warm colours**. Green and blue are known as **cold colours**.

In graphics, warm colours appear to come towards you from the page, but cold colours appear to recede.

Test yourself

1 Name the secondary colours and give the primary colours that make them.

2 Describe the meaning of colour harmony and colour contrast.

Enhancement techniques

Check the facts

Numerical data has to be presented in a way that makes things clear and accurate. It is important that the right sort of chart or graph is used and this can depend on the type of information. Examples of different sorts of charts and possible uses are given below.

Analysis of predicted grades

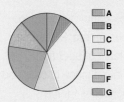

PIE CHART
This type of chart is useful for showing fractions of a whole number. It is possible to create 3D pie charts and extract the segments.

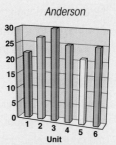

Anderson

BAR CHART
This type of chart is useful for showing numbers of people who choose various options (e.g. colour choices). This chart is in 3D form, but could be in 2D. Different colours of bars can be used on the same chart.

Summer module tests

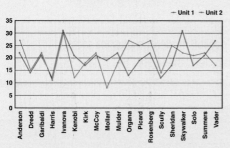

Summer module tests

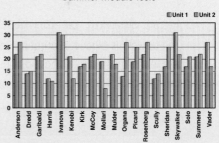

These two graphs show the same information in different forms (a line graph and a bar graph). They both show results obtained by students in two different tests. The information is clearer in the bar chart. Line graphs are good for showing simple results over a period of time, e.g. how well a product sells. Another form of chart is a **pictogram**. These use small pictures of relevant objects, e.g. cars on a traffic survey, to show quantities.

BBC GCSE Check and Test: Graphic Products

Test yourself

1 Name three different types of chart or graph.

2 Why is a line graph good for showing how well a product sells in the course of a year?

Check the facts

Backgrounds

Using coloured paper or card is an easy way of making a background. Pale colours are better than bright colours. Backgrounds can be produced using a colour wash or pastels. ICT can also be used to produce a background.

Mounting work

Drawings can be mounted on paper or card. **Surface mounting** is where the drawing is fixed directly to another piece of paper or card. Sometimes double mounting is used. This uses two different colours of backing material. **Window mounting** is where a hole is cut into a piece of card and the drawing mounted behind. If using squares or rectangles for the drawings or for windows, make sure they are cut with straight edges and are fixed parallel to the edges of the sheets.

Adhesives

Avoid the use of liquid glues, as they may squeeze out under the artwork and cause the paper to wrinkle. Spray adhesives, rubber-based adhesives and double-sided adhesive tape are all good methods. Adhesive sticks are useful for small pieces of work.

Heat sealing or laminating

The artwork is placed in a transparent 'pocket' made of a plastics material. It is fed into a machine that has heated rollers. These seal the plastic over the artwork.

Test yourself

1 Name two methods of mounting graphics work.

2 Why should liquid adhesives not be used when mounting artwork?

Enhancement techniques

www.bbc.co.uk/revision

Check the facts

The tools used in model-making depend on the materials used, the type of model and the finish required. The chart below lists the main tools that are used.

Type of model	Materials	Marking out tools	Cutting tools	Finishing tools
Card models	Card	Pencil, ruler, set squares, compasses.	Craft knife, cutting mat, safety ruler, scissors.	Not required.
Plastic sheet models	Foam board, styrene sheet, corrugated plastic.	Pencil, fine line felt pen, steel rule, try square, set square.	Craft knife, cutting mat, safety ruler, snips.	Use the edge of a knife blade to scrape the edges of styrene sheet. Use glass paper on edges of foam board.
Solid 3D models	Styrofoam, medium density fibreboard.	Pencil, steel rule, try square.	For styrofoam – tenon saw, coping saw, craft knife, safety ruler, band saw (teacher use only), jig saw. For MDF – tenon saw, wood chisel, bench hook, band saw (teacher use only), jig saw.	For styrofoam – files, glass paper. For MDF – rasps, plane, glass paper, sanding machine.

Test yourself

1 Name three tools that could be used when marking out foam board for a large 3D model.

2 Describe how styrofoam could be cut and finished when making a model of a mobile telephone.

Model-making techniques

BBC GCSE Check and Test: Graphic Products

Model-making techniques

Check the facts

The chart below shows a range of processes that can be used in model-making and the types of models that might be produced by that process. The type of process used will depend on the sort of model required. For some models, it will be necessary to use a range of materials and processes.

Process	Description	Main materials	Type of model
Fabrication	Joining of individual parts using adhesives or technical components.	Card, foam board, styrene sheet and strip, styrofoam, MDF, plywood, timber strips.	Pop-ups, point-of-sale displays, solid product models, interior design models, small fabricated models in styrene. Larger fabricated models.
Forming	Forming thin plastic sheet by bending in a straight line or by vacuum forming.	Styrene sheet, high density PVC, acrylic.	Any type of model which may need a line bend, or where a 3D shape needs forming.
Moulding and wastage	Moulding a form from pliable materials, using plaster bandage over a former, using styrofoam.	Clay, plasticine, plaster bandage, styrofoam, block MDF.	Solid product models. Models of landscapes and gardens, models of figures and free shapes, moulds for vacuum forming.

Test yourself

1 Name two different processes that could be used to make a solid block model of a portable CD player.

2 Name a process that could be used to make a model of 'bubble' or 'blister' packaging.

Check the facts

A range of modern materials used for graphics are described below.

Treated papers are available for modern computer printers, especially for ink jet printers. This will absorb the ink and allow a good colour reproduction.

Thermochromic pigments are in paste form and can be added to any acrylic-based medium. At normal room temperature, they appear coloured but at 27°C the colour disappears. It will reappear when the temperature falls.

Phosphorescent pigment can be mixed with a white acrylic base. The pigment absorbs light and will then glow after the light source has been removed.

Thermocolour sheet is a sheet material printed with thermochromic liquid. It will change colour when heated above 27°C.

Polymorph is a plastics material that fuses and becomes mouldable at 62°C. It can be used for product modelling for applications such as handles and making simple moulds for vacuum forming, especially where curved shapes are involved.

High density modelling foam is a foam-based material available in blocks. It can be shaped easily with hand and machine tools and takes fine detail well. It is often used on CNC milling machines.

Test yourself

Describe the properties of the materials listed below and give examples of their use:

1 polymorph

2 high density foam.

New materials

Systems and control

Check the facts

A **system** is a set of components arranged to carry out a particular function. Systems can consist of **mechanical, electrical** or **electronic components**. Some systems will combine components from more than one of these groups. Systems can also refer to the way in which products are made. This is a **production system**, but will still include the terms described below.

> Systems consist of separate sections – **input, process** and **output**. Many systems also involve the use of **feedback**.

The input is what goes into the system. In a music centre, the **input** comes from a record or CD player, a radio tuner or a tape player. The **process** part of a music centre is the amplifier. The **output** is the speakers connected to the amplifier. **Feedback** is used to set the volume. If the music is too loud, the user will reduce the volume.

In a **production** system, the input is in the form of raw materials. The process is the shaping and forming of the materials and the output is the finished product. Feedback is in the form of checking that the product meets the specification.

Test yourself

The stages of producing a school newsletter are shown below, but not in the right order.

Secretary types newsletter.
Form tutors give out copies to students.
Headteacher dictates newsletter.
Secretary sorts copies and sends to form tutors.
Students take pictures with digital camera.
Draft is checked by Headteacher.
Students take newsletters home.
IT technician assembles text and pictures.
Reprographics technician prints copies.

1 Identify the inputs and outputs.

2 Identify where feedback is used.

Check the facts

Equipment used for graphic design involves the use of **feedback** and **control**. The chart below gives some examples.

Equipment and type of system	Control	Feedback example
Rotary paper trimmer – mechanical system	Speed of movement of cutting blade. Cutting fence can be set to required distance – allows repetition.	Paper cut is ragged – blade may need sharpening/replacing, cut fewer sheets. Wrong size – reset fence.
Computer printer – electronic/mechanical system	Number of copies, paper type, quality of print-out. Repetition through repeat copies.	Number of copies wrong – reset on computer. Quality of print poor – change paper or ink cartridge.
Photocopier – electronic/mechanical system	Size of copy/ enlarge/reduce, number of copies. Number of copies made, type of paper or other materials, quality of print out. Copy too dark/light.	Size is wrong – reset size. Number of copies wrong – reset number required. Quality of print poor – change paper or toner cartridge. Contrast wrong – adjust contrast control.
CAM 2D card/vinyl cutter – electronic/mechanical system	Speed/depth of cut, pressure on cutter order of cutting. Repetition though repeating process.	Cutting incorrect – adjust speed, depth, pressure through software or hardware controls. Order wrong – reset though software controls.
CAM 3D milling machine – electronic/mechanical system	Speed/depth of cut, rotational speed of cutter, type/size of cutting tool, order of cutting. Repetition though repeating process.	Cutting incorrect – adjust speed, depth, through software or hardware controls. Order wrong – reset though software controls.

Test yourself

List examples of feedback and how work can be altered as a result of feedback on the following items of equipment:

1 rotary paper trimmer **2** photocopier.

Systems and control

BBC GCSE Check and Test: Graphic Products

Check the facts

It is possible to analyse a system to identify the inputs, processes and outputs and where feedback occurs.

Analysis of a system

You need to look at the system to identify the input, process and output. The blocks below show the inputs, the process stages, the output and where feedback happens for the system described in topic 73.

INPUT	PROCESS	FEEDBACK	PROCESS	PROCESS
Headteacher dictates newsletter.	Secretary types newsletter.	Draft is checked by Headteacher.	Reprographics technician prints copies.	Form tutors give out copies to students.
Students take pictures with digital camera.	IT technician assembles text and pictures.		Secretary sorts copies and sends to form tutors.	

OUTPUT
Students take newsletters home.

A similar analysis can be done of a mechanical system. In the drawing on the right, the input will be the movement of someone's hand opening the card. The process will be the movement of the card's parts. The output will be the scene standing upright.

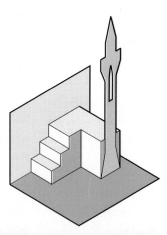

Test yourself

Work out the inputs, processes and outputs in the systems shown:

1 making a cup of tea

> Fill kettle.
> Switch on power.
> Has water boiled?
> Make tea.

2 cam toy.

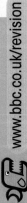

Check the facts

- To design your own system, first decide what the output required is. This will probably be some sort of **motion** – linear, rotary, reciprocating or oscillating (see topic 77). You also need to decide on the force required for the output.

- Then decide what the input motion will be – again, one of the four types of motion given.

- You can now make a decision about the process part of the system. This could involve the use of levers, cams, cranks, pulleys or gears (see topics 78–81). The direction of the movement may also have to be changed.

Other design decisions:

- How can moving parts be supported?

- How will the systems be powered?

- How can friction be overcome?

- What is the degree of accuracy required?

Once these decisions have been made, you can design it on paper and model it before making in suitable materials.

Test yourself

The drawing below shows elements of a pop-up book on the theme of space and a description of the type of movement required. Decide what mechanical systems should be used to give the required movements.

1 The drawings above show some of the phases of the moon. The large blue circle represents the Earth. Design a mechanism to show the four phases.

2 This drawing shows a simple design of a space rocket. Design a mechanism that will allow it to be shown as a 3D form in a pop-up book.

Systems and control

BBC GCSE Check and Test: Graphic Products

Check the facts

> **There are four types of motion that can be used in mechanical systems.**

Rotary motion – turning round in a circle, e.g. a wheel turning.

Linear motion – moving in a straight line, e.g. on a paper trimmer.

Reciprocating motion – moving backwards and forwards in a straight line, e.g. cutting with a saw.

Oscillating motion – swinging from side to side, e.g. a pendulum in a clock.

Changing the direction of motion

These types of motion can be changed into another type by the use of mechanisms. The chart below gives a summary of these methods of changing motion.

Type of change	Mechanism to use
Linear to rotary and rotary to linear	Wheel and axle, rack and pinion, rope and pulley, screw thread
Rotary to reciprocating	Crank, link and slider, cam and follower
Reciprocating to rotary	Crank, link and slider
Rotary to oscillating	Crank, link and slider, cam and follower, peg and slot
Oscillating to rotary	Crank, link and slider, peg and slot
Reciprocating to oscillating	Rack and pinion, crank, link and slider
Oscillating to reciprocating	Crank, link and slider, cam and follower

Test yourself

1 Name the type of motion change shown in the drawing on the right.

2 Name the type of motion of a pendulum in a model clock used to help young children tell the time.

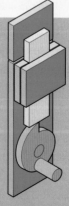

Check the facts

- Levers are used to transmit a force from one place to another.

- A set of levers is called a **linkage**.

- Linkages can be used in a number of different products, such as pop-up cards and books, point-of-sale displays and other products with moving parts.

Design decisions about levers

- How much force has to be transmitted? What is the amount of load and effort?

- What is the direction of the output force compared to the input force?

- Which class of lever will be used? What are the relative positions of load, fulcrum and effort?

- What material will the lever be made from? Is the material sufficiently rigid and strong?

- How will the fulcrum be made and supported?

- How will the effort be applied? By hand or by mechanical means?

Test yourself

The drawings below show two design situations where lever systems could be used to provide the desired movement. Draw a possible solution to each situation.

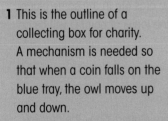

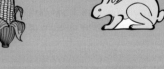

1 This is the outline of a collecting box for charity. A mechanism is needed so that when a coin falls on the blue tray, the owl moves up and down.

2 This is the outline of a moving picture in a story book. A mechanism is needed so that the rabbit moves across to eat the corn.

Systems and control

BBC GCSE Check and Test: Graphic Products

Systems and control

Sometimes it is necessary to draw out the moving parts of a mechanical system to ensure that it fits in the space required. When the end of a lever moves, the shape it draws out is called a **locus**. The way in which this is done is shown below. In this example, the drawing shows the movement of a point, labelled O, as the mechanism moves.

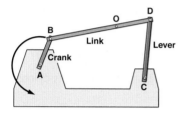

This drawing shows the outline of the mechanism. The crank rotates anti-clockwise as shown by the arrow.

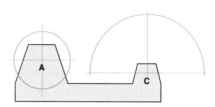

1 Draw a circle, radius AB, centre at A. Draw a semi-circle, radius CD, centre at C.

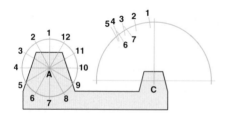

2 Divide the circle into twelve equal parts. Number each one. Set compasses from distance B to D. Put point at number 1 and mark arc 1. Repeat for other divisions as shown.

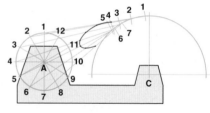

3 Measure distance BO along lines and mark points. Draw a freehand curve through the points as shown by the black line above. This is the locus of point O.

Note that in the example above, some of the arcs are in the same place on the semi-circle, but the marks showing the locus of point O will be on different lines.

In the example above, only half the points are plotted. Copy the drawing and complete the locus for all twelve points of rotation.

www.bbc.co.uk/revision

Check the facts

- A **pulley wheel** is a wheel with a groove around the outside to take a driving belt.

- Pulleys are used to transmit rotary movement from one place to another.

- The axles for pulleys can be parallel or at 90° to each other.

- Pulleys can transmit motion over a considerable distance by using only two pulleys.

- An **open driving belt** will cause two pulleys to turn in the same direction.

- A **crossed driving belt** will cause two pulleys to turn in opposite directions.

- A driving belt turned through an angle can be used when the axles are not parallel.

- Traditional driving belts can slip. Modern toothed pulley wheels and belts will not slip, but the belts cannot be crossed or angled.

Design decisions about pulleys

- How much power has to be transmitted?

- How will the axles be supported? What will the bearings be made from?

- How will the power be applied? By hand or by mechanical means?

- What material will be used for the driving belt?

- Will bought-in components be used or will the pulleys be made?

Test yourself

The drawings below show two design situations where pulley systems could be used to provide the desired movement. Draw a possible solution to each situation.

— motor

1 Draw a pulley system that would allow the motor to turn the vertical rod. The rod should turn three times slower than the motor.

2 Draw a pulley system that would turn the sails of the windmill when the handle is turned. The sails should turn twice as fast as the handle.

Systems and control

BBC GCSE Check and Test: Graphic Products

Systems and control

Check the facts

- A **gear wheel** is a wheel with teeth round the outside that lock into the teeth on an adjacent gear.
- The teeth are often called **cogs**.
- Types of gears include:
  spur gears – axles must be parallel
  bevel gears – axles can be at an angle to each other
  worm and worm wheel – axles must be at 90° to each other
  rack and pinion – a rack is a gear in a straight line.
- Gears are used to transmit rotary movement from one place to another.
- Gears are used to transmit motion over short distances.
- Two gears working together will turn in opposite directions.
- If three gears are working together, the ones on the ends will turn in the same direction.
- Gears will not slip.

Design decisions about gears

- How much power has to be transmitted?
- How will the axles be supported? What will the bearings be made from?
- How will the power be applied? By hand or by mechanical means?

Test yourself

The drawings below show two design situations where gear systems could be used to provide the desired movement. Draw a possible solution to each situation.

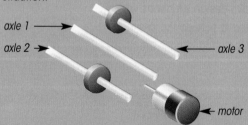

axle 1
axle 2
axle 3
motor

1 Show how spur gears could be used to connect the motor to the axles. Axle 1 should go four times slower than the motor. Axle 2 should go twice as fast as axle 1. Axle 3 should go three times slower than axle 1.

2 Which type of gear could be used to connect two axles at 90° to each other? One must turn at half the speed of the other.

Check the facts

Electrical systems can be used in graphic products in various ways, as listed below:

- Product design models may use switches and LEDs to make the product more realistic.
- Point-of-sale displays may need electric motors to turn parts in a rotary motion.
- Point-of-sale displays may have lighting units built into them.

Some common symbols for electrical components:

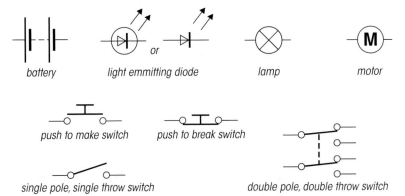

| battery | light emmitting diode | lamp | motor |

push to make switch   *push to break switch*

single pole, single throw switch   *double pole, double throw switch*

Components are usually placed on **printed circuit boards** (PCBs). The board is made from **Paxolin**, which is a plastics material, and is coated in a thin copper sheet. When a PCB is made, the copper is etched away using an etching solution such as ferric chloride, except where the copper is covered with a substance that resists the etching solution. For simple circuits, the etch resist can be a special felt pen or rub-down transfers. More complex boards can be produced by a photographic process.

Test yourself

1 Using the symbols above, draw a circuit for a torch that uses a lamp, battery and a suitable switch.

2 The drawing below shows part of a reversing switch circuit for an electric motor. Copy the circuit, name the components and complete the circuit.

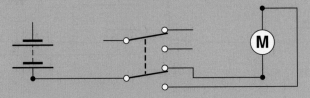

Check the facts

In order to make a circuit board layout, the theoretical circuit needs to be translated into a practical circuit. The drawings below show a simple circuit of battery, switch, LED and resistor.

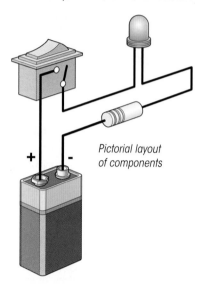

Pictorial layout
of components

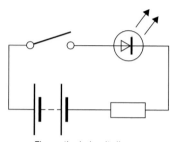

Theoretical circuit diagram

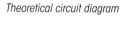
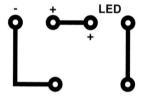

PCB layout (copper side)

The drawings above show the pictorial layout, circuit diagram and the layout of tracks on the circuit board. One of the most important things to remember when drawing a circuit layout is that the components are on the opposite side to the copper tracks. This means that some connections are reversed on the copper side.

Test yourself

The drawing below shows a reversing switch circuit for a motor that uses a battery and a double pole, double throw switch. Design a circuit board layout for this circuit.

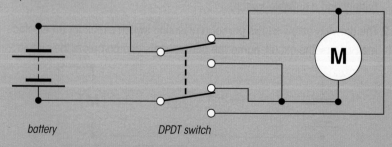

battery   DPDT switch

Check the facts

Systems are important in industry since they help to ensure that tasks are done in the correct order and that materials are available when required. The chart below shows what is involved in the production of a batch of printed leaflets.

INPUTS	PROCESS	OUTPUT
Brief from customer.	Printing of sample copies.	The product.
Artwork from designer.		Paid employees.
People who do the work.	Checking quality – a form of feedback.	A customer who is pleased with the result.
Materials – paper and ink.	Adjust printing machines as required.	
	Print batch.	

When planning a manufacturing system, the following types of activity have to be considered:

Storage of raw materials, bought-in components, sub-assemblies and part-finished products.

Inspection of:

- bought-in components to make sure they are of the required quality
- part-finished products to ensure they meet the specification
- checking of artwork.

Inspection must be done at all the crucial points in the production process.

Operations: processes of making that have to be planned into the system.

Movement of raw materials, part-finished products and complete products has to be planned.

The symbols listed below can be used for these different activities:

Storage   *Inspection*   *Operation*   *Movement*

Test yourself

Using the symbols above, draw a systems diagram for the printing of the backing card for a 'blister' or 'bubble' pack for a toy vehicle.

Systems and control

BBC GCSE Check and Test: Graphic Products

Check the facts

There are two types of chart that are useful for planning the order of work for a graphic product. These are **flow charts** and **Gantt charts**. They can be used for the planning of your project, or for planning work in industry. The drawings below show examples of both types.

Systems and control

Flow chart

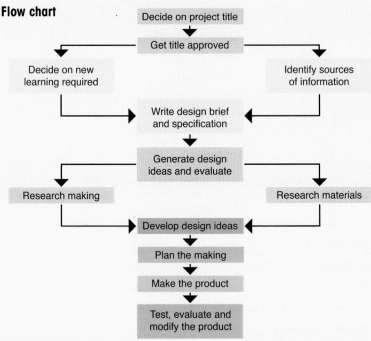

Decide on project title
↓
Get title approved

Decide on new learning required

Identify sources of information

Write design brief and specification
↓
Generate design ideas and evaluate

Research making

Research materials

Develop design ideas
↓
Plan the making
↓
Make the product
↓
Test, evaluate and modify the product

Gantt chart

Week 1	Week 2	Week 3	Week 4	Week 5	Week 6	Week 7	Week 8	Week 9	Week 10
Decide project title, get title approved.									
	Identify new learning required and sources of information, brief and specification								
		Generate design ideas & evaluate							
			Research materials and making						
				Develop design ideas					
						Plan the making			
							Make the product		
									Test, evaluate, modify

Test yourself

Make both a Gantt chart and a flow chart for a piece of work you have done during your GCSE course.

Check the facts

Product design analysis involves a detailed examination of the following aspects of a product:

- The function and purpose of the product.
- What the different parts of the product are and how they work together.
- How the product actually works and any scientific principles involved.
- The materials used to make the product.
- The processes used to make the product.
- The intended market for the product.
- How well the product does its job when compared with other similar products.

Some of these aspects apply when looking at existing products before designing your own. In the examination, product design analysis is usually tested by looking at photographs or drawings of existing products and written information about them.

How to be successful at product design analysis

- Make sure you understand what the product actually does and how it works.

- Learn how products are made in industry – especially what sort of materials are used and how they are cut, shaped, formed, joined and finished. Apply this knowledge to the product you are asked to analyse.

- Think carefully about possible markets for different products. Who would buy the product? Why would they buy it? Where would it be used? Who would use the product?

 Test yourself

This drawing shows a model theatre with scenery and figures. The figures are made to move by rods attached to their bases.

1 Name the main materials used for the model theatre and the figures. Name a suitable material for the rods used to make the figures move.

2 Name a suitable printing process that could be used to print the parts of the model theatre.

Quality in designing and making

BBC GCSE Check and Test: Graphic Products

Quality in designing and making

Check the facts

There are two aspects to quality in design and technology:

- **quality of the design itself** – how well the product meets the needs of the user
- **quality of the manufacture** – how well the product has been made.

These two aspects of quality can be independent of each other. A product can be designed well but be poorly made. A well-made product may be of a poor design which does not meet the needs of the user.

Example

A pop-up book may be designed well and look attractive but could be poorly made with rough edges, inaccurate cutting of the moving parts and poorly made joints of the pages. Alternatively, it could be well made but the card used may be too thin to stand up to the movement required.

To ensure good quality in a product, the designer should check that:

- it meets the needs of the user
- appropriate materials are used
- where necessary, the product is capable of being maintained in good condition
- making is planned carefully to ensure that checks for quality are made at the appropriate time
- making is done carefully and accurately
- the use and disposal of the product after use have been considered.

Test yourself

This drawing shows the packaging for a cake.

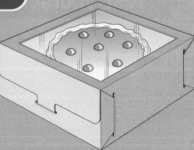

1 State why you think the materials used for the box are appropriate.

2 Why is there a transparent window in the lid of the box?

3 How could the box be made so that the cake inside is not damaged when it is being taken home from the shop?

Check the facts

A **quality product** will fully meet the needs of the user. In order to ensure quality in meeting needs, find out exactly what the user requires. This can be done in a number of ways:

- talking to the user

- thinking carefully about what the user needs

- observing the user

- asking questions

- looking in books and magazines that illustrate the lifestyle of the user.

Not all of these points will be suitable for every situation. It may be difficult to talk to young children about what their needs are for different sorts of toys, but a designer could look at them at play and see what sort of toys they like to play with. A designer could also talk to parents or other adult helpers about what might be suitable.

Having identified exactly what the needs of the user are, they should be accurately recorded. When developing possible ideas, the designer should constantly refer back to the user needs to ensure a quality product.

Test yourself

A large public building, such as a library, a school or a hospital, needs signs and maps to help people find their way around.

1 List the people who use the signs. Remember those who buy the signs, fix them in place and who maintain them and keep them clean.

2 List the needs of the people who use the signs.

Quality in designing and making

BBC GCSE Check and Test: Graphic Products

Quality in designing and making

Check the facts

A quality product will use materials and components appropriately. In order to ensure quality in the use of materials and components, a designer needs to do the following things:

- make a list of the properties and qualities that the product requires the materials to possess

- collect information about materials and components that may have these properties, and samples that could be examined and tested

- carry out research into the properties and do tests on samples to see how closely they meet the requirements

- consider cost, working properties, maintenance and availability as part of the research and, where appropriate, what the user thinks

- make a decision based on all the relevant factors about the best materials and components for the purpose.

Test yourself

Packaging for a breakfast cereal could be made from one of the following:

- a waxed paper bag inside a cardboard box
- a foil-lined card box
- a flexible bag made of a plastics material, such as cellophane
- a rigid plastic box made of a plastics material such as polyethylene.

List four aspects of these materials that should be considered when deciding which would be best to use from a quality point of view.

www.bbc.co.uk/revision

Check the facts

A quality product will be made using the most appropriate manufacturing processes. Checks will be planned to ensure that manufacturing is of the best possible quality.

In order to ensure quality in manufacturing, a designer needs to do the following things:

- research the most effective ways of working with the materials that will be used

- check to ensure that those involved in the making have the necessary equipment and skills to do the manufacturing to the agreed level of quality

- ensure that those involved in the making are aware of the degree of quality required for the product

- devise and use checks on quality at regular intervals or at critical points in the making processes

- ensure that bought-in components are made to the required quality level and are checked

- ensure that the cost of the final product is sufficient to meet the quality standards of making which are proposed

- make a decision based on all the relevant factors about the best methods to be used.

Test yourself

A set of menus for a restaurant is required. The menus could be made by any of the following processes:

- produced on a black and white photocopier

- produced on a colour photocopier

- produced using letterpress printing

- produced using offset lithography

- produced by gravure printing.

List four aspects of making that should be considered when deciding which would be best to use from a quality point of view.

Quality in designing and making

BBC GCSE Check and Test: Graphic Products

Quality in designing and making

Check the facts

Values in design and technology include **technical** values, **moral** values, **cultural** values and **environmental** values. A quality product will be designed to ensure that value issues are considered and, where possible, acted upon.

In order to ensure quality in the application of values, a designer needs to consider the following points:

- **Technical values** – ensure that the manufacturing methods and materials used are accurate and result in a reliable product.

- **Moral values** – ensure that the product meets a defined need and does not cause offence to others.

- **Cultural values** – ensure that the product does not undermine the views of other cultures.

- **Environmental values** – ensure that the making, using and disposal of a product after use do not adversely affect the environment.

Test yourself

Consider one of the following products:

1 packaging for a music centre

2 an adventure game

3 signs at an open-air pop concert.

List two aspects of each of the values mentioned above that should be considered by the designer.

Check the facts

A designer needs to consider aspects of health and safety when designing.

Safety of the finished product when it is used

- Will the product be strong enough to support the loads involved?
- Are the materials suitable for the purpose? (No adverse effects, toxic, harmful, and so on.)
- Are all hazards sufficiently guarded? (Electrical insulation, moving parts, folding components, and so on.)

Safety of the finished product when disposed of after use

- Can the component parts and different materials be dismantled without harm?
- Will dismantling result in the release of toxic or harmful substances?
- Will recycling of materials cause release of toxic or harmful substances?

Safety during the making of the product

- Will any of the materials specified cause harm to the maker?
- Will any of the processes used cause harm to the maker?
- Will any of the finishing techniques used cause harm to the maker?

> If any of the aspects listed above are likely to cause harm, then that aspect of the product will need redesigning.

Test yourself

List one safety point (three in total) to be considered when using, disposing of and making one of the following products:

1 a floor-standing point-of-sale display for books to be used in a shop

2 a disco set for use by a band at a school disco.

Health and safety

Check the facts

All those involved in the making of products have a responsibility to use safe working techniques in order to avoid harm to themselves or others.

Safety when making involves:

- safe storage and use of tools and equipment, including the use of machines
- safe storage and use of materials, chemicals, finishes and solvents
- safety in the use of flammable and toxic substances.

To ensure safety when making, use the following procedures:

- Store tools and equipment so that sharp edges and cutting blades are protected. Isolate power tools from the electrical supply.
- Operators should be fully trained in the use of tools and equipment.
- When using equipment, personal protective equipment should be used. It should also be used by other workers nearby if necessary.
- Ensure all guards and other protective devices are in place at all times when the equipment is in use.
- Materials must be stored so that sharp edges and ends cannot cause harm.
- Wear gloves when handling materials with sharp edges.
- Store all chemicals, inks, paints and solvents correctly in accordance with the manufacturer's instructions. Some materials may need special storage away from other substances.
- When using toxic or flammable substances, use personal protective equipment. Take care to avoid excess contact with toxic substances and to turn off naked flames when flammable substances are used.

Test yourself

List one safety point (three in total) to be considered in the following situations:

- cutting card with a craft knife
- using a disc sanding machine when making a product design model
- spray painting a product design model.

www.bbc.co.uk/revision

Check the facts

The following are provided in order to ensure personal safety for makers, both in industry and in schools and colleges:

- personal protection equipment – overalls, gloves, eye protection, ear protection, barrier creams

- guards on machines

- extraction systems for dust and toxic fumes.

All organisations have a responsibility to supply suitable protective equipment where it is required. Such equipment has to be kept in good condition. All workers, including those in schools and colleges, have a responsibility to use the equipment provided.

Personal safety has to be considered in the disposal of waste materials, including chemicals and solvents. Where necessary, chemicals should be neutralised by appropriate chemical processes. Some materials may need to be stored in special containers and collected by licensed waste disposal contractors.

Test yourself

List personal protection procedures needed when carrying out each of the following processes:

- cutting and shaping high density polystyrene
- using spray paint to paint a product design model
- using a computer workstation.

Health and safety

BBC GCSE Check and Test: Graphic Products

Health and safety

Check the facts

Risk assessment is the process of considering the hazards that could arise in a particular situation and the risk of someone being hurt.

A **hazard** is defined as anything that is likely to cause harm and/or damage.

The **risk** is defined as the chance that the hazard may cause harm and/or damage.

Risk assessment is defined as how likely it is that harm or damage will be caused.

When planning the making of a product, a designer may need to carry out risk assessments relating to materials, processes or finishes. Regulations and technical information should be consulted to identify the potential hazards.

Ideally, the hazard should be eliminated totally. Where this is not possible, the hazard should be reduced by the use of protective equipment, such as guards on machines, extraction systems or personal protection equipment.

If the hazard cannot be reduced to an acceptably safe level, the process should not be carried out.

Test yourself

Identify one risk involved when carrying out each of the following processes, and then state a way in which that risk could be reduced:

- using a craft knife
- storage of printing inks
- use of electrically powered equipment.

Check the facts

Health and safety in relation to environmental effects is concerned with the following points:

- chemicals used in the making or finishing of products

- the disposal of products after use

- the recycling of materials and components.

When designing products, designers need to consider how adverse environmental effects can be avoided. This may mean the use of alternative processes, materials or chemicals. The use of alternatives may mean that some parts of the product need to be redesigned or an alternative manufacturing process used.

Current concerns about the environment mean that the disposal of products after use has to be considered in the initial design. Methods of separating components and recycling materials also have to be built into the design.

Packaging materials form a large part of waste and have to be disposed of. Designers may have to think of alternative ways of packaging, such as moulded and compressed card rather than expanded polystyrene, or reduce the amount of packaging required.

Test yourself

Products can be packaged by using moulded, compressed card packaging and packaging chips that can be dissolved in water. List three things a designer would have to consider if this method of packaging were to be used.

Health and safety

BBC GCSE Check and Test: Graphic Products

Check the facts

Usually designers produce ideas for products in response to market forces. Sometimes this is called **consumer pull**.

Examples of market influences include:

- a demand from consumers for new or improved products

- a competing product is launched by another manufacturer

- a manufacturer wants to increase their share of the market.

Products may also be redesigned because of changes in materials or manufacturing methods. This is sometimes called **technology push**. Technological changes may allow a manufacturer to make the product more cheaply, or more efficiently, thus reducing manufacturing costs.

Occasionally, a designer will design a new or improved product simply because they feel it is needed or because a demand will be created by the very existence of the product, e.g. Sinclair ZX Spectrum personal computer, Dyson cyclone vacuum cleaner. Such a development may succeed or fail, depending on the market.

Test yourself

Adventure and board games are a popular leisure activity. Sometimes an existing game will be remodelled to meet a new demand. List some market influences that could influence the design of a new type of game.

Designers and consumers

Check the facts

When designing graphic products, it is important that images and text should not cause offence to other people. It is also important that production methods should not harm the lifestyles of people or their working abilities.

When designing, the following points should be considered:

Images and text
Some people could be offended by certain sorts of images and/or text. Public images, such as films, advertisements and similar products, have to be designed so as not to cause offence. Private images, such as greetings cards, may only be seen by the purchaser and the recipient and, in such cases, images and text, which may not be acceptable to all, may be produced since they are not on public view.

Cultural influences
Different cultures have a rich and diverse heritage of graphic images and these may be a source of ideas for new products. Different styles of text and particular ranges of colour can also be used.

Use of natural resources
When designing and making, natural resources in other countries may be over-exploited. Paper is a major natural resource for graphic products and should be supplied from sustainable forests. There needs to be a balance between the use of recycled materials and the need for new materials.

Test yourself

List the advantages and disadvantages of using recycled materials in graphic products.

Designers and consumers

BBC GCSE Check and Test: Graphic Products

Designers and consumers

When designing graphic products, it is important that environmental issues are taken into account. The following points should be considered:

Source and production of raw materials

The production of paper and card makes use of **cellulose fibre**, which is normally obtained from wood, old rags or old paper. If made from wood fibres, care needs to be taken to ensure that wood from sustainable sources is used. The processes of paper-making may produce waste products that pollute the environment. Printing inks are produced by chemical processes and care has to be taken to ensure that waste products do not cause pollution.

Manufacturing processes

Some manufacturing processes may cause harm to the environment. Printing machines need to be cleaned and the cleaning solvents have to be disposed of safely. Waste inks also need to be disposed of in the correct manner.

Products

Graphic products themselves may cause harm to the environment. The disposal of unwanted packaging is a particular problem, although card can easily be recycled. Paper from unwanted newspapers and magazines can also be recycled, although some types of paper can cause problems.

Test yourself

List four ways in which a graphic designer can reduce harm to the environment.

Check the facts

Some graphic products have to comply with legal requirements. These are set out below.

Packaging

Packaging for all products has to state where the product was made, what it is made from, how it should be used and any safety hazards. The weight should also be stated. In addition, packaging for food has to include the name and address of the manufacturer, the name and description of the food, the ingredients, storage and cooking instructions and nutritional information.

Leaflets and books

The name of the printer has to be shown. For books, details have to include copyright permission for text and illustrations.

Health and safety

Health and safety is a legal requirement. Graphic products have to be safe to use and dispose of and should be capable of being made safely. Care needs to be taken about things such as lids, tops and pouring devices, to make sure that sharp edges are not exposed when the packaging is opened. The materials used for food packaging should not contaminate the product.

Test yourself

List four things that are legally required to be included on a food label.

Answers

01 Writing a design brief

1 Open brief Design a way of displaying sunglasses in a shop so that they can be displayed in an attractive manner and tried on easily. Closed brief Design a point-of-sale display for sunglasses which can be used to display the products attractively but enable them to be easily removed for trying on. The display should fold flat and be assembled without the use of tools or adhesive.

2 Open brief Design the packaging for luxury chocolates that are going to be a special present. Closed brief Design packaging for a new range of luxury chocolates called 'Light and Dark'. The packaging should hold a maximum of twelve chocolates and enable the content to be seen without the lid being opened.

02 Writing a specification

Specifications should include all the relevant information from page 7.

1 The information guide has to clearly show a person how to assemble the product. Each page should not be larger than A4 size. White or coloured paper should be used. The guide should mainly use pictures or symbols. Words should not be used if the user cannot understand the language. The product will only be used once so it does not have to be robust and the cost should be as low as possible. The pages need to be usable without turning over to relate instructions to text or symbols. The guide should be able to be mass produced to match the number of products sold. Legal information about consumer rights may have to be included. As the leaflet will be thrown away after use, it should ideally be made from recyclable materials.

2 The graphics and controls should be laid out in such a way that the function of each one is clear. Symbols rather than words should be used. The size of the symbols will have to relate to the size of the controls, or the available space. Symbols should be understood by any possible user. They may have to be able to be understood by people in any country in the world. The product will probably be made from thermo-plastic which has been shaped by injection moulding. This will affect the design and the interface. Anthropometrics and ergonomics are very important in this product – size of control

buttons, space between them, force needed to operate, etc. The cost of the interface should not be substantial since it will be included in the cost of the whole product. The product will be mass produced so the interface must also be capable of being mass produced. The materials should be capable of being recycled when the player is no longer needed.

03 Developing initial ideas

1

2

04 Developing the chosen idea

Possible materials Thick corrugated card as used in packaging. Corrugated plastic sheet, sometimes called 'Correx' or 'Corruflute'. For a smaller model, foam board or mounting board. Cutting and shaping methods Use a craft knife with safety ruler and cutting mat. Joining methods Single or double-sided adhesive tape. Tabs and slots for card. For Correx or Corruflute, plastic rivets can be used.

05 Using modelling to develop ideas

1 Card, thin clear plastic sheet, adhesive tape.
2 Foam board, balsa wood, wire, card.
3 Solid foam, styrene sheet, wooden dowel rod.

06 Planning the making of a product

Mark out the various parts on the foam board using a sharp pencil and a ruler.   15 mins
Cut to shape using a craft knife, safety ruler, and cutting mat.   30 mins
Use fine glasspaper to smooth the cut edges.   10 mins
Paint the parts with the base colour as required (includes drying time).   60 mins
Mark out the decoration on the back walls.   30 mins
Paint the decoration (includes drying time).   60 mins
Assemble the various parts with glue and leave to dry (includes drying time). 60 mins
Touch up paint and add fine details as required.   30 mins

07 Equipment for drawing

1 Protractor
2 Pair of compasses
3 T-square or parallel motion

08 Using colour media

1 Water soluble coloured pencils
2 Gouach
3 Spray paints

09 Making two-dimensional models

1 Flat card model
2 Construction kit
3 Sketch drawing

10 Making three-dimensional models

1 Card or plastic sheet model
2 Computer modelling
3 Solid foam or MDF

11 Printing techniques – screen printing

1 Posters, T-shirts, cushion covers, display boards, wall paper, control panels.
2 To allow the ink to come through.

12 Printing techniques – block printing

1 Greetings cards, wall paper, paper table cloths and similar products.
2 Because a new block would have to be made for each colour.

13 Printing techniques – using colour

1 Cyan, magenta, yellow and black.
2 Lithography
3 To make sure each colour lines up.

14 Finishing processes

1 Varnishing, laminating.
2 Embossing
3 Book covers, photo albums.

15 Photographic equipment

1 35 mm still camera, instant camera, digital camera.
2 The image can be seen instantly. The image can be manipulated using a computer and suitable software. Processing of films is not required.

16 CAD and CAM

1 Input devices Keyboard, mouse, scanner, digital camera, drawing tablet, tracker ball. Output devices Printer, plotter, plotter/cutter, CNC lathe, CNC milling machine, stereo lithography machine.
2 2D products Drawings for making products, packaging design, labels for packaging, standard and pop-up cards, information signs, advertising material, leaflets, books, pop-up books, information sheets, posters.
3 3D products Mock-up of consumer products, quick prototypes of design ideas, point-of-sale displays, designs for interiors, prototype models.

17 Using ICT for drawing

1 Bitmap software 'draws' in pixels.
2 Vector software 'draws' in coordinates.
3 Drawings can be changed and resized easily, ready-made drawings can be modified, standard components can be 'imported' into a drawing.

18 Using ICT for desktop publishing

1 To create page layouts quickly and easily.
2 To allow text and images to be moved around the page.

19 Using ICT for modelling

1 2D drawing software with text manipulation function.
2 So that the shape and appearance can be seen from all viewpoints.

20 Using ICT for making

1 It allows complex shapes to be made easily and accurately. Changes can be made quickly and easily. The product can easily be mass produced.
2 Complex shapes, including curves, can be made easily. Fine detail can be machined. A good finish can be produced.

21 Using ICT in industry

1 The time from idea to prototype is reduced. Changes can be made quickly and easily. The computer can simulate what the final product will look like.
2 It allows a realistic image of the final product to be seen.

22 Understanding commercial manufacturing systems

One-off Special cards, special books, signs in buildings and in the street, shop identity signs, room interiors. Batch production Special cards, special books, signs in buildings and in the street, short printing runs, e.g. business stationery, short packaging runs, point-of-sale displays, pop-up books. Mass production Cards, books, posters, magazines, newspapers, board games, user interfaces. Continuous flow Books, posters, packaging.

Answers

BBC GCSE Check and Test: Graphic Products

Answers

23 Commercial manufacturing systems 1
1 'Plastic' bottles.
2 Thermo-plastic

24 Commercial manufacturing systems 2
1 Products with fine detail: bottle caps, casings for mobile phones, radios, CD players, etc.
2 Thermo-plastic

25 Printing methods – letterpress
1 Business stationery, special invitations, menus, programmes.
2 The time taken to set up the printing plate. Limitations on style of fonts available.

26 Printing methods – lithography
1 Magazines, posters, packaging and book printing.
2 To allow the ink to stick to the areas to be printed.

27 Printing methods – flexography
1 Carrier bags, some types of wall paper, food packaging.
2 Because it will print on the materials used for packaging food, e.g. polythene.

28 Printing methods – gravure
1 Magazines, mail-order catalogues, packaging, fabrics, wall paper, postage stamps, plastic laminates.
2 To press the paper into the cell on the plate.

29 Printing techniques – cutting and creasing

30 Printing techniques – photocopiers
1 Takes a range of different sizes of paper – A5 up to A3, takes card and clear acetate as well as paper, will enlarge and reduce, will do back to back copying, will collate sets of material.
2 Paper sizes Different sizes of a graphic product can be produced. Materials Art work can be printed on different materials, acetate is good for tracing and similar tasks. Size Different sizes of artwork can be produced. Back to back Good for mock-ups and the final product.

31 Packaging methods and techniques
1 To contain and hold the product, to protect the product from damage, to inform the customer about the product, to help promote and sell a product, to make it convenient to carry, use and store.
2 a DIY products such as small tools, shelf brackets, nails, screws, drill bits, toys, etc.
b Food products, soft drinks.
c Alcoholic drinks, soft drinks, food products.

32 Marketing and advertising a product
The package could include the following: information about what the product can do, information about what the product is made from, information about a special price offer.

33 Quality control
Are the various parts made accurately, e.g. shape, size, methods of joining? Is any printing required in the correct place? Have the correct colours been used? Do the various parts fit together correctly? Does the point-of-sale unit stand up correctly and does the product fit?

34 Time-planning charts
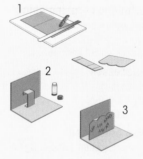

35 Testing and evaluating products
Use the points listed in the topic to check your answer.

36 Evaluating a finished product
Use the points listed in the topic to check your answer.

37 Checking to ensure a product meets value considerations
1 Card Technical Is it well made? Have appropriate materials and finishes been used? If there are moving parts, do they move correctly and smoothly? Moral Do the images on the card cause offence? Has it been made of recyclable materials?

Can it be recycled after use? Cultural Why do we need such a card? Do the images conform or conflict with other cultures? Environmental What is the source of the materials? Do they come from sustainable/renewable sources? What energy sources have been used in the making? How are waste products disposed of?

2 **Plastic bottle** Technical Is it well made? Does it hold the drink hygienically? Have appropriate materials and finishes been used? Does the bottle or label contain the required information about the product? Moral Has it been made of recyclable materials? Can it be recycled after use? Cultural Why do we need soft drinks? Do the images conform or conflict with other cultures? Environmental What is the source of the materials? Do they come from sustainable/renewable sources? What energy sources have been used in the making? How are waste products disposed of?

3 **Board game** Technical Is it well made? Have appropriate materials and finishes been used? Do the counters or game figures have sharp edges? Are the materials safe to use? Moral Do any images or game rules cause offence? Has it been made of recyclable materials? Can it be recycled after use? Cultural Why do we need such a game? Do the images conform or conflict with other cultures? What about the concept of winners and losers? Environmental What is the source of the materials? Do they come from sustainable/renewable sources? What energy sources have been used in the making? What happens to the game when it is no longer needed?

38 Checking that materials have been used appropriately

Check your answer against the points given in the topic.

39 Checking that processes have been used appropriately

Check your answer against the points given in the topic.

40 Materials used in graphic products
1 White card about 350 microns
2 Bleedproof paper

41 Materials used for model-making
1 Rigid foam or MDF

2 Foam board or thick card

42 Plastics used in graphic products
1 Polystyrene sheet
2 Corrugated polypropylene

43 Adhesives used in graphic products
1 Spray adhesive, glue stick, double-sided tape.
2 To make a 'mask' for spraying paint or when airbrushing.

44 Obtaining a good finish on models
1 Scrape the edges with a steel rule. Use silicon carbide paper to smooth the edges. Polish on a buffing machine or with metal polish.
2 Sand the surfaces carefully with fine glass paper. Apply plaster to fill any gaps. Sand when dry. Paint with acrylic paints or water-based paints.

45 Printing inks
1 The colourant and the vehicle.
2 Because of different printing processes and different materials on which printing is done.

46 Standard components – lettering techniques
1 Self-adhesive paper labels. Dry transfer lettering. Raised plastic lettering.
2 Advantages Wide range of fonts and styles. Easy to do. Disadvantages Limit on size of paper in printer. Letters may have to be glued to the product.

47 Standard components – fastenings and found items
1 Paper fasteners are useful for moving parts in pop-up books and models.
2 Rubber bands are useful in pop-up models and crash lock boxes to give a 'spring return' action.

48 Standard components – mechanical components
1 Pulleys will transmit power over a longer distance than gears. Both systems will give a range of speeds. Pulley belts can slip. Gears will not slip. Gear systems may be more complicated to set up.
2 Use a gear box or pulley system to provide a slow speed.

49 Standard components – fastenings
1 Joining pieces of wood. Construction of the frame of a point-of-sale unit. Construction of a large scale model of a

sign system. Making moving joints in large section wood.

2 The wood may split if wood screws are used. The nuts could be tightened to make the frame stay in one place.

50 Sketching techniques
1 To allow complex shapes to be drawn easily.
2 So that ideas can be drawn quickly.

51 Orthographic projection
1 To allow complex objects to be drawn with all the necessary detail.
2

52 Assembly drawings
1 To show how something is put together. To show the position of different parts of a product. To allow a set of parts to be assembled.
2 The parts of a product are shown taken apart, but in the correct positions for assembly.

53 Section drawings
1 To show how something is put together. To show what the inside of a product looks like. To make the construction of the product clearer.
2 The product is drawn as if some parts are cut away.

54 Isometric drawing
1 30°
2 Sketches and notes should resemble the drawing in the topic.

55 Planometric drawing
1 45°
2 Because the drawing can be done from a plan view and exactly to scale.

56 Perspective drawing
1
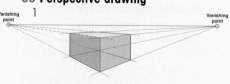
Vanishing point   Vanishing point

2 Because the drawing looks more realistic.

57 British Standard symbols
1 Symbol as shown in topic.
2 Compression spring

58 Dimensions on drawings
1 Extension line
2 Turned so they can be read from the right.

59 Two-dimensional geometrical shapes – three and four sided
1 Sides and diagonals are of equal lengths. No 90° corners.
2 Equilateral triangle

60 Two-dimensional geometrical shapes – polygons and circles
1 All sides are the same length. All angles are the same size. The exterior angle is 72°.
2 A sketch showing the parts, as shown in the topic.

61 Ellipse construction
You could draw a half ellipse using the major axis as the base, or a half ellipse using the minor axis as the base. You should leave in all the construction lines so that an examiner can see how you have done the construction.

62 Three-dimensional geometrical solid shapes
1 The ends are triangles. The sides are rectangles.
2 Rectangle

63 Surface developments or nets
1 The ends are circles. The side is a rectangle.
2 Six sides would be required.

64 Surface developments or nets – pyramids and cones
The final drawings should resemble the drawings in the topic.

65 Enhancing the appearance of a drawing
The final drawings should resemble the drawings in the topic.

66 Showing texture on a drawing
The drawings should be similar to those in the topic.

67 Colour
1 Orange – red and yellow; green – blue and yellow; violet – red and blue
2 Colour harmony Colours that are next to each other on a colour wheel. These colours go well together. Colour contrast Colours on opposite sides of a colour wheel. When placed side by side, these colours contrast with each other.

68 Presentation of data
1 Bar chart, pie chart, scatter diagram, star chart, line graph, pictogram.

2 Because the number of sales in a month can be seen. Changes can easily be seen.

69 Presentation techniques
1 Surface mounting, window mounting.
2 Because the liquid will cause the paper to wrinkle up.

70 Tools used in model-making
1 Pencil, ruler, set squares, compasses.
2 Cutting large pieces – use a bandsaw. Cutting smaller pieces – use a tenon saw, coping saw, jig saw, craft knife. Finishing – use files and glasspaper.

71 Model-making methods
1 Fabrication from styrene sheet. Shaping a block of MDF by wasting methods.
2 Vacuum forming

72 Making use of modern materials
1 Polymorph is a plastics material that fuses and becomes mouldable at 62°C. Used for moulds and curved shapes which can be shaped by hand.
2 HD foam is a dense foam material good for CNC machining since it will take fine detail.

73 Systems used in products
1 Inputs Head teacher dictates newsletter. Students take pictures with digital camera. Outputs Reprographics technician prints copies. Students take newsletters home.
2 Draft is checked by Headteacher.

74 Control systems on graphics equipment
1 Rotary paper trimmer Feedback will be the size of the cut sheet and the quality of the cut. Alterations as a result: reset fence, check position. Quality of cut: slow down cutting speed, check sharpness of cutter.
2 Photocopier Feedback will be in the form of quality of print, contrast, size/number of copies. Alterations as a result: check toner and contrast settings, check size settings check number of copies setting.

75 System analysis
1 Input Fill kettle with water. Process Switch on power. Output Boiling water.
2 Input Turn the handle. Process Cam turns. Output Top part moves up and down.

76 Mechanical systems design
Any suitable mechanism that will do the job is correct, but the following ideas are possible: For the phases of the moon – a sliding mechanism with the earth moving in front of the moon. For the rocket – a V fold or layer mechanism would work.

77 Types of motion
1 Rotary to reciprocating
2 Oscillating motion

78 Using lever systems
1 A lever system connected to the tray would cause the owl to move.
2 A rotating lever would give the required result. A slider mechanism would also work.

79 Drawing the movement of mechanical systems
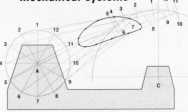

80 Using pulley systems
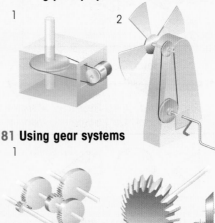

81 Using gear systems
1

2 Bevel gears: one gear must be twice the diameter of the other.

Answers

82 Electrical systems in graphic products

1

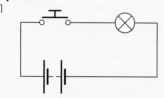

2

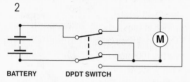

BATTERY   DPDT SWITCH

83 Planning and drawing electrical circuits

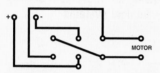

MOTOR

84 Using systems when making graphic products

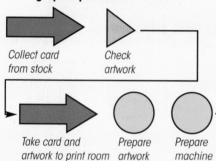

Collect card from stock   Check artwork

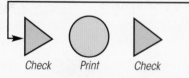

Take card and artwork to print room   Prepare artwork   Prepare machine

Check   Print   Check

85 Using charts for planning manufacturing

Suitable charts that are similar to those in the topic.

86 Product design analysis

1 The theatre and figures could be made from good quality card similar to mounting board. It could also be a solid white board. The main criteria is that the card should take inks well. The rods could be made of wood or a plastics material.

2 Lithography

87 Quality in designing and making

1 The card is lightweight, it can be printed and cut to the shape easily. It can be supplied in a flat form to save space in transport and storage. It can have a waxed surface to give a hygienic surface.

2 The transparent window allows the customer to see the type of cake.

3 The sides could be made of a double layer of card. The tabs that join the sides would make it stronger.

88 Ensuring quality in meeting needs

1 Users Visitors, staff (especially new staff), purchasing officer, maintenance staff, cleaning staff.

2 Visitors Signs must be clear, easy to read, visible, illuminated if outside. Staff As for visitors. Purchasing officer Signs must be low cost, robust, long lasting, easy to clean, easy to fix and maintain. Maintenance staff Signs must be lightweight, easy to fix, easy to maintain. Cleaning staff Signs must be easy to clean and keep clean, accessible for cleaning.

89 Ensuring quality in the use of materials and resources

Is the material appropriate to the task? How easy will it be to cut, shape, form, join and print the material? Can the material be disposed of safely after use? Will the material affect the food product?

90 Ensuring quality in manufacturing

Is colour required? Would the photocopied menus be sufficiently robust to last? Would the quality be appropriate? Will the printing processes available be compatible with the type of card required, or can appropriate card be found which will suit the process? Is embossing required and can it be done? Does the number of menus required justify the costs of plate making and printing?

91 Ensuring quality in meeting values

1 Technical values Does it protect the product from damage? Is the text on the outside box clear and accurate? Moral values Is all the packaging necessary? Can alternatives be used? Can the packaging be re-used? Environmental values What happens to the packaging when the product is unpacked? Can it be recycled?